Research and Development Management

RESEARCH AND DEVELOPMENT MANAGEMENT

by

THOMAS W. JACKSON
Research Professor of Mechanical Engineering,
Associate Dean of Engineering-Research,
and Chief, Mechanical Sciences Division
Georgia Institute of Technology
Atlanta, Georgia

and

JACK M. SPURLOCK
Chief, Engineering Research Group
Atlantic Research Corporation
Alexandria, Virginia

1966

DOW JONES-IRWIN, INC.
HOMEWOOD, ILLINOIS

First Printing, June, 1966
Second Printing, September, 1969

Library of Congress Catalog Card No. 66–24594

PRINTED IN THE UNITED STATES OF AMERICA

Preface

Since World War II, research has grown into a multi-billion dollar activity. Perhaps it was the technological shock experienced by the world when the first atomic bomb was exploded over Hiroshima that precipitated the avalanche of money into what is called research. Perhaps it is the space-age education and the threat of annihilation to which the public is exposed that makes it possible for the taxpayers' dollars to be diverted into research. Whatever the reason, research has become "Big Business" and as such it deserves careful scrutiny by those persons interested in knowing how it works and how the funds being allocated to it may be obtained.

This book should appeal to managers of technical laboratories, technical analysts, project directors, and project engineers in current research activity. It is also visualized that this book may be used as a text or supplementary text for courses in industrial management, business administration, and industrial engineering. Military hardware contractors may find it particularly interesting if they desire to enter into research and developmental activities. It is intended that the structure of this book will elucidate for the reader the steps necessary in establishing a research and development capability, administering this capability, and sustaining a creative output.

If the book is utilized as a text, it is suggested that the following procedure be followed:

1. Divide the lecture periods during the semester by the number of chapters.
2. Allocate this number of lectures to each chapter. The first lecture on each chapter should cover the material given in this effort.
3. Make up the remaining lectures by discussing and lecturing on references selected from those given for the chapter.
4. Utilize the questions for each chapter and selected readings from the bibliography as homework assignments.

If the above procedure is followed, the students will obtain an overall picture of research and development operations. The details of the picture may not be deep; however, astute students will obtain an appreciation of research and development which might otherwise take them years to develop.

This book would never have been completed without the inspiration the authors received from Dr. A. A. Potter, Dean Emeritus of Engineering, Purdue University. The authors gratefully acknowledge his suggestions, editorial help, and encouragement.

Atlanta, Georgia   T. W. JACKSON
Alexandria, Virginia   J. M. SPURLOCK
May, 1966

Table of Contents

Chapter 1

Introduction to Research and Development Objectives

"WHAT IS RESEARCH?" Each researcher has his own ideas on this subject. On reflection he can define research; however, when his definition is compared with others it will be found that definitions vary from individual to individual.

In order to have a basis for discussion in this book, the following generalized definition of research is offered for consideration:

Research is carefully oriented and organized investigation which seeks to extend current knowledge through the analytical and experimental discovery and use of new facts.

A fact is that which has actual existence and, consequently, research involves the formation of conclusions from the use of facts. In other words, research is a search for better ways of doing things and for new knowledge. Research covers many and various types of activities. It can be simple and involve the discovery of a single fact; it can be complicated and involve exhaustive examination of many facts in order to cast new light on a complicated phenomenon. The broadness of the definition of research has caused various adjectives to be applied to define, in a

1

more specific manner, the type of work that is meant. For instance, fundamental research, applied research, and developmental research are terms commonly experienced by one who makes his career on the frontiers of science and engineering. These terms define, in more detail, segments of the total scientific and engineering research picture.

The interrelationship among these various segments is illustrated in Figure 1–1. The double arrows which

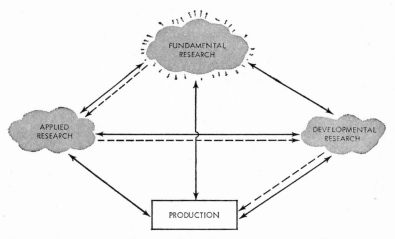

Fundamental Research—Studious Inquiry into Basic Phenomena
Applied Research—Endeavor to Understand Basic Phenomena
    and Apply the Results to a Useful Purpose
Developmental Research—Endeavor to Create Methods and
    Tools to Produce a Useful Product
Production—Generation of Useful Product for Market

FIG. 1–1

INTERRELATIONSHIPS AMONG FACTORS INVOLVED IN THE CREATION
OF A USEFUL PRODUCT

connect the segments of the figure indicate the reason why the term research has various meanings to different people. A fundamental idea may be sufficiently sophisticated that its commercial product can be placed into production without going through the evolutionary processes of applied and developmental research. Likewise production problems may indicate the need for fundamental research effort. In most cases, however, the usual evolutionary process, indicated by the dotted lines, will apply. The fundamental research establishes the true character of a phenomenon or concept. The applied research extends the understanding of the basic phenomenon, determines its practical significance, and directs this new knowledge toward the creation of a feasible idea for a useful application. The developmental research creates the methods and tools for the production of any resultant product. Finally, production actually generates the item for market.

To insure economic returns from industrial research, the laboratory results must be put to work. Merely reporting research results in reports or in papers before learned groups may be adequate in the case of fundamental or basic research, but industrial and other applied research must be followed by development, pilot and field testing, and technical promotion to insure commercialization in a competitive market at a profit. For every dollar spent in applied research, many dollars must be available for translating the research results into marketable products.

Fundamental Research

Fundamental, by definition, is that which underlies all outward manifestations and is ostensibly permanent. Fundamental, or basic, research is the studious inquiry conducted to understand the basic phenomena of nature. One of its primary aims is to broaden our knowledge base, with little or no concern for the use which will be made of the new knowledge. In fact, one of the basic research organizations of the Department of Defense states in its guidelines brochure that an investigation in which predictable results are sought *is not basic research.*

Although fundamental research is unpredictable and may not net immediate dividends to the researcher or research organization, nevertheless, it is significant that basic research resulted in discoveries which led to practical uses of atomic energy, radar, radio astronomy, synthetic fibers, plastics, antibiotics, hybrid corn, etc. The discovery that lightning was electricity was very basic and Ben Franklin is to be congratulated for performing an excellent research job with a key, a piece of string, and a kite. Outside of the publicity with which this work was endowed, it is doubtful if any other tangible reward accrued to benefit Mr. Franklin. In fact, it is amazing that the researcher was not killed while conducting the experiment. Today, however, many persons owe their livelihood to the basic idea that lightning is electricity. Farmers buy lightning rods to protect their homes and farm buildings. Even large skyscrapers such as the Empire State Building must have protection from lightning. The discovery that lightning was electricity thus formed the basis for a whole new industry.

Whereas fundamental research seemingly has no immediate payoff to its sponsor, from the long-range view it is the fountainhead for new technology. The fact that one concept, generated from fundamental research effort, can give rise to a large number of products through the evolutionary process of applied and developmental research is illustrated in Figure 1–2. This figure shows the chain reaction for the growth of a basic concept into numerous product applications.

Most of the basic or fundamental research is conducted

in universities by professors and their students. The reason for this is twofold; first, the university is a seat of knowledge which attracts the individual who is inquisitive about how nature works; and second, the professor

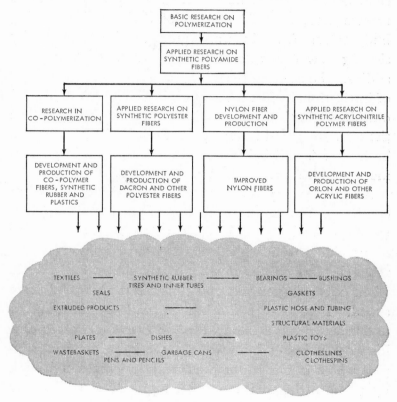

FIG. 1–2

THE CHAIN REACTION OF A BASIC IDEA

does not have the economic necessity of "making a profit" hanging over his head. This last statement is fast becoming obsolete because many of the large universities are now doing research as a business and, as a business (research for money), an economic motive hangs over the work like a sword of Damocles.

A well-known past science adviser to the Secretary of

State emphasized the fact that an economic motive exists in universities. He pointed out that too many educational institutions seem to have drifted into the enterprise of handling research contracts rather than education. Going further, he stated that several universities receive more than 50 percent of their total operating budgets from federal research grants, with one university signing new contracts at the rate of five per day. In addition, he asserted that this produces an overemphasis of institutional effort towards goals which are established outside the institution and which must necessarily reduce the effort required for the proper education of students. This issue is still being argued on both sides in government as well as private circles.

A close scrutiny of many campuses indicates a trend to emphasize the more profitable applied and developmental endeavors. As a result, many professors are no longer doing work which can be defined as fundamental research. One professor who is still doing basic work, when queried as to what purpose his work would serve stated, "I don't care if it's ever used—I just want to understand what is happening." It is not surprising that his work is being done without the large financial support which is given to applied and developmental work by sponsors who are interested in a product for defense or space applications, or for profit.

Under the necessity of producing a product for given amounts of money and time, the fundamental researcher soon becomes an applied researcher. This transition is hurried by the research proposal, which the research organization employs to interest the potential sponsor. The proposal, in order to be salable, must state what is to be done, how it will be done, how much it will cost, and finally what the results are expected to be. In other words, the research program must be delineated prior to its start and, consequently, if anything basic is obtained from the work it will probably result from lucky coincidence. This is not as bad as it seems since many of the people doing research do not have the creative talent for conducting basic investigations.

Basic research, however, must be encouraged or progress will be stifled. This is indicated in the words of a prominent industrial leader, "Unless there is a revolutionary change in attitude about basic research in U.S. industry, there will come a day when there is no use trading in your old car . . . because the new one is no better." Characteristically, industry not only delegates much of the responsibility for basic research to colleges and universities, but it also expects government support to finance the bulk of this effort. The director of a large university research center predicted in 1961 that: "The next ten years will see a growth from the current (1961) rate of $130,000,000 per year to approximately $400,-000,000 per year in U.S. engineering college research." Commenting on the role of industry, he said,

. . . over the past ten years direct research support from industry has remained essentially constant while that of government has more than tripled. If this process takes place again over the next ten year period, we will find an even smaller percent of industry support and a greater dominance of government support in our research sponsorship . . . already representing 85 percent of sponsored research support. Industry is losing a fine opportunity to keep in direct touch with our professors and graduate students by failing to carry their normal share of engineering college research support.

One of the finest results of basic research is illustrated by the story of nylon. Dr. Carothers of the DuPont

Company pursued a fundamental program of research to understand the structure and mechanism of polymers. This work was apparently started without the necessity to predict its results or possible products. Yet, as is the case in most successful basic research, useful items resulted from the work. The chief product, nylon, became the basis for a completely synthetic textile industry. In addition, from applied research on nylon in the past few years a wide variety of applications, such as nylon tubing, bearings, structural members, and gears, have been developed. The returns on the initial investment, which was essentially a gamble on basic research, are self-evident.

Not every company can afford to subsidize fundamental research since for every successful venture many unfruitful expenditures of time and effort are common. In general, in order to finance basic or fundamental research, sufficient liquid assets, which can be used without danger or risk to the financial solvency of the company, must be available. Consequently, most basic research is left to the colleges and universities. They are in turn being encouraged to do more applied research by financial pressures of outside sponsorship. Fortunately, each of the Department of Defense segments (Army, Navy, and Air Force) and other Government agencies have been far-sighted enough to establish agencies primarily for the purpose of encouraging basic research in the sciences. These agencies and the branches of science which they support will be discussed later.

Applied Research

Before the phenomenon, discovered by the basic researcher, can be turned to a practical use it must be understood and defined in practical terms. The endeavor to extend the understanding of basic phenomenon, determine its practical significance and develop useful applications is called applied research. In applied research which precedes product development, one of the common principal goals is the generation of a prototype product item. In many cases, however, the principal effort of the applied research is directed towards understanding the basic phenomenon being investigated in order to obtain sufficient engineering information for use in the design of a prototype.

Applied research is intermediate between the discovery of the basic phenomenon and the generation of a final product. It too, like fundamental research, does not return immediate dividends to the researcher or research organization; however, because a reason for the work is evident, the possibility of attaining financial rewards from the work is greater than in the case of basic research. In many cases the applied research effort is done by organizations which did not discover the idea or ideas on which their applied research is based. Therefore, these groups are able to produce salable products and results with a much higher probability of financial reward. Of course, the fact that they can stay in business depends on the base of knowledge that is available to them. This supply in the past has stemmed from ideas developed in universities and by individuals who have creative talent. The modern trend in many large corporations is to support their own basic research groups in order to build up a stock pile of fundamental ideas on which to base their applied and developmental research endeavors. This type of operation accelerates the development of the state-of-the-art of a company's product line and assures it a leading place in the competitive market. Many progressive firms have current products which were unknown and inconceivable ten years ago. This fact emphasizes strongly to management the necessity of having a superior research organization. Those companies which do not have a research capability soon discover, to their sorrow, that they are reworking and reworking old ideas based upon passé product lines. This process breeds sterility and death in the competitive market place.

A principal problem in many industrial organizations is a misinterpretation and downgrading of the role of applied research in the overall effort of generating a new product. The large cost of the developmental effort and the fact that it immediately precedes the actual production of the product tend to make production managers forget that applied research did much to pave the way for the new venture. The large developmental costs soon eat into applied research budgets much to the despair of applied researchers. The applied researchers soon begin to feel that they have created a "Frankenstein monster" which is cannibalistic and has started to devour its creators. To prevent this difficulty a constant effort must be made by top management personnel to maintain a balance between applied research and developmental endeavor to assure that neither feeds at the expense of the other. When an unbalanced situation develops, unrest and dissatisfaction among creative research people usually results; and the company often loses irreplaceable talent. If balance is not soon restored, the loss of talent will produce harmful effects on the company's growth. Examples of this process are, unfortunately, too numerous to cover in this text.

Many different types of investigation can be categorized as applied research. For example, a very important facet of applied research in many of the larger companies and in a few of the more progressive smaller companies is market analysis. This vital endeavor tunes the manufac-

turer in on the desires of his customers. The importance
of market research was emphasized by Charles R. Bea-
cham of the Ford Motor Company in his comment "We
can build anything if we can find out what people want."
Any investigative effort which seeks to provide new
results directly applicable to a useful product or purpose
can be categorized as applied research.

Developmental Research

Developmental research involves the creation of methods and tools to produce a product. A prototype item,
often the product of applied research, is still, in many
cases, not ready for actual production processes. After
applied research creates an item that will work and do a
satisfactory job, developmental research must recreate
and refine this item and build production systems so that
it can be manufactured in an efficient, economical, and
rapid manner. The investigation of polymers, which led
to the discovery of nylon, was fundamental research. The
determination of the critical properties and characteristics of nylon and its potential uses in the textile and
various other industries was applied research. The development of efficient methods, machinery, and equipment to produce nylon in various forms and shapes for
industry was developmental research.

The role of developmental research should not be
underrated. A developmental program can, to a large
extent, determine whether or not the research that has
gone on before will be profitable. It should be pointed
out that the organization or company undertaking the
developmental program need not have funded or worked
on the first two phases of the evolutionary sequence of
events from a basic idea to a product. In many cases,

items which have been developed to a feasible prototype stage by applied research efforts have been kept out of the commercial market by lack of economic methods to put them into the hands of the consumer. Developmental research, therefore, is an important step in the evolution of an idea into a finished product.

Exactly where applied research ends and developmental research begins is not as clearly defined as has perhaps been implied in the foregoing. Developmental research often feeds information and orientation back into applied research and even into basic research as indicated in Figure 1–1. Many problems or knowledge shortcomings can arise during a developmental program. These problems may require basic or fundamental investigations. More often they may require additional applied research to provide sufficient resolution to permit effective continuation of the developmental program.

There is magic in the word *research*. Perhaps the wonders created in its name during the past hundred years are justifications for the reputation the word has obtained. To the researcher, however, *research* has still another attraction—it is a challenge. The basic researcher is often disinterested or only partially interested in profitable returns on the investment in his project. The challenge the research problem poses is his main motivation. To him, finding a solution to the problem is a game which is to be played for enjoyment; if, at the same time, the game produces a useful result, this is an extra bonus. In many cases, the basic researcher will do the work despite all obstacles including personal financial problems. This is another reason why it is not entirely detrimental for government and industry to require that researchers outline their programs, give methods of solution, and indicate expected results prior to the funding of the work. These requirements are perfectly logical for applied and developmental programs. However, they are often too stringent for basic research efforts and a more general outline of a program should be required for purely fundamental projects. Of course, an astute researcher can satisfy sponsor requirements and leave himself enough freedom to play his research game, thereby satisfying both interests involved.

In evaluating the relative merits of the various types of research, it should be remembered that they are all about equally important. Research ideas, without the backing of applied and developmental efforts, have little utility; applied and developmental efforts, without basic new ideas, are sterile.

Basic research, as stated before, is partially a game which the researcher plays with nature. This game is also played by the applied researcher and even the development engineer.

The main difference between the three research phases is in their separate abilities to attract financial support. Whereas the basic researcher often has little interest in the financial aspect of his work, the applied researcher is searching for a useful end result, and the development engineer is aiming his efforts at production from which substantial financial rewards may be obtained. Consequently, an applied researcher has an advantage over the basic researcher in obtaining funds to carry on his projects. He is closer to the production phase in the research evolution picture and his work is attended by a somewhat smaller financial risk. Developmental research, being still closer to the production phase, has even less difficulty in obtaining funds for supporting the effort.

Usually, large companies anxious to put a product on

the market will spend millions of dollars developing new machinery and setting up new production processes. These investments are usually recovered in short periods of time since research which has reached the developmental stage is likely to yield economical results. However, the threat of failure is always present and it may stem from the development of a competing process or machine in the hands of a competitor. In this case the consumer usually benefits at the expense of the company who backed the losing research effort. Although some of the research will have been wasted on useless effort, through feedback into basic and applied research, portions of the effort may be recovered and used on other and different processes or applications.

As can be seen from the foregoing discussion, research is a very complicated process. It evolves, it has an end, and it regenerates itself. Today the overall research effort is more important than ever before. The enormous increase in the world's population of over fifty million per year makes it imperative that new and more efficient means of supplying the necessities of life be found at an ever increasing rate if the majority of the world is not to sink into a morass of want. But it is evident that the rapid growth of research and the exponential growth of population cannot continue indefinitely. Sooner or later a tapering off must take place.

Research Expenditures in the United States

The pinch of competition has sent U.S. industry and government on a gigantic quest for new products. The result has been the growth of annual research and development expenditures from $2.5 billion in 1950 to over $20 billion in 1965. Figure 1–3 indicates that by 1970 the expenditure of research and development funds will be near a $30 billion per year rate. Figures of this magnitude suggest to the small business man that he should undertake research and development programs, but he tends to recoil from research ventures and feels that they are only for government and large corporations. The

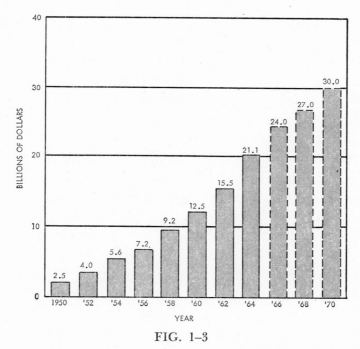

FIG. 1–3

RESEARCH AND DEVELOPMENT EXPENDITURES, 1950–70

facts are, however, that small as well as big businesses who have responded to new product ideas through research have profited greatly from their investments. In many cases companies that have used their research funds wisely and efficiently are no longer small companies. It should be pointed out that the success of basic and applied research endeavor depends on the creative talents of selected individuals. If a creative person is availa-

ble, large returns on small initial investments are possible. In contrast, the developmental phase of research
can be extremely expensive. The requirement for wise
decisions in screening and selecting research and development projects and personnel to work on them should not
be underestimated. This is especially true if the support
is to be derived from company funds. If, however, government support can be obtained then even the small
company is in a better economic position since immediate returns on the expenditures are not necessary for
survival.

In selecting the research problem for government
support, the requirements of the government are of
prime importance. Decisions as to the details of the
problem and methods of solution are jointly the responsi-

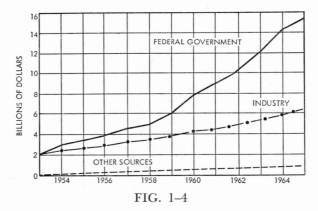

FIG. 1–4

SOURCES OF RESEARCH AND DEVELOPMENT FUNDS,
1953–65

bility of the company's representatives and the technical
or project administrator of the government. In this
respect it is interesting to examine the contribution of
the federal government to the funding of research and
development programs performed by private industry.
Figure 1–4 indicates the annual sources of monies fund-

ing the overall research and development (R and D) effort of the United States, and Figure 1–5 is an index to the actual performers of the work. It is readily evident from the figures that the government financially supports much of the work and industry performs most of it. The

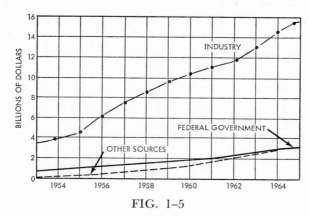

FIG. 1–5

PERFORMERS OF RESEARCH AND DEVELOPMENT, 1953–65

actual percentage distribution between federal and company funds expended by industry for R and D performance for 1961 is shown in Figure 1–6. Figure 1–7 shows actual company R and D expenditures in 1961. By using the percentages in Figure 1–6 and the actual expenditures given in Figure 1–7, it can be seen that most of the funds are concentrated in relatively few industries. Over 50 percent of the total $6.5 billion of federal funds spent for industrial research was accounted for by the aerospace industry; 23 percent of the total by the electrical and electronics industry; over 3 percent by the chemical process industry; about 4 percent by the machinery industry; and about 3 percent by the automotive and other transportation equipment industry. These five industries accounted for over 80 percent of the federal R and D funds spent by industry in 1961.

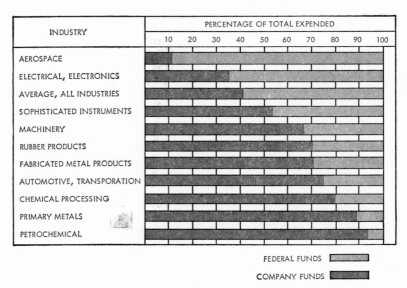

FEDERAL FUNDS

COMPANY FUNDS

FIG. 1–6

PERCENTAGE DISTRIBUTION OF FUNDS EXPENDED BY VARIOUS INDUSTRIES FOR RESEARCH AND DEVELOPMENT PERFORMANCE, BY SOURCE, 1961

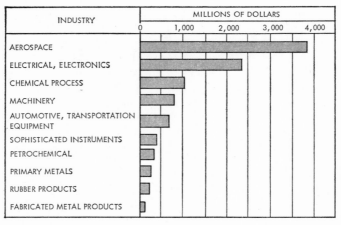

FIG. 1–7

FUNDS EXPENDED BY VARIOUS INDUSTRIES FOR RESEARCH AND DEVELOPMENT PERFORMANCE, 1961

Many industries expend a limited portion of their own funds for research; company-financed research and development, by industry, in 1960 and 1961 is illustrated in Figure 1–8. Although the chemical process industry spent approximately $875 million in 1961 on research and development, the corresponding expenditure for

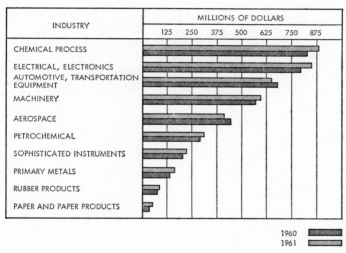

FIG. 1–8

COMPANY-FINANCED FUNDS FOR RESEARCH AND DEVELOPMENT, BY INDUSTRY, 1960 AND 1961

basic research was considerably less. The funds expended for basic research performance by industry in 1961 are illustrated in Figure 1–9. This figure also indicates the relative contribution of funds from federal and company sources for industrially performed basic research.

As has been shown, federal funds for research and development are concentrated in a few industries which contribute to the bulk of military equipment and defense production. The government, to assure a continuous flow of basic research, is contemplating increasing its nonmilitary research and it can be anticipated that the budget of the National Science Foundation and the National Institutes of Health will increase materially in the coming years. The National Science Foundation is primarily interested in the funding and support of basic or funda-

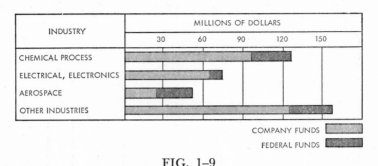

FIG. 1–9

SOURCES OF FUNDS FOR BASIC RESEARCH PERFORMANCE, BY INDUSTRY, 1961

mental research; however, the definition of applied research used herein will probably cover some of the work which is supported by this Foundation.

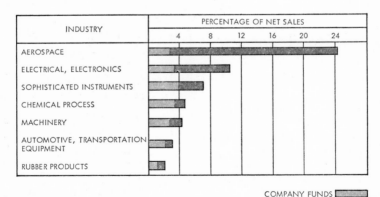

FIG. 1–10

SOURCES OF TOTAL RESEARCH AND DEVELOPMENT PERFORMANCE FUNDS AS PERCENTAGES OF NET SALES IN MANUFACTURING COMPANIES, BY INDUSTRY, 1961

The distribution of research and development funds, by source, for typical industries as percentages of the net sales in 1961, is shown in Figure 1–10. The average value for total R and D funds was 4.4 percent of net sales in 1960 and was unchanged in 1961. This represents a slight increase over the 4.1 percent for 1959. Company-financed research and development in companies with R and D programs increased from 1.7 percent of net sales in 1959 to 1.9 percent in 1961.

In Figures 1–3 through 1–10, statistical data have been presented up through the latest year for which reliable survey information was available. The reader can maintain a current profile of these statistics by reviewing the several documents published periodically by the National Science Foundation (e.g., see References for this chapter).

Summary

A viewpoint on the general aspects of research and development has been presented. The overall area of research and development, like Caesar's Gaul, is divided into three parts or subareas: fundamental (or basic) research, applied research, and development (or developmental research). Fundamental research is primarily concerned with the search for scientific knowledge with little regard for the application of this knowledge to the generation of a specific useful product. However, the results of this type of research usually serve as the fountainhead for future scientific and engineering endeavor in the evolution of useful products. Applied research combines, refines, and extends the results of fundamental research to obtain practical technology which will serve a useful purpose or generate a useful product. In the latter case, applied research often results in the design of a prototype device or process. Developmental research is concerned with the refinement of applied research results and the integration of these with production and processing methods which will most efficiently and economically generate the product for market.

The demarcations between the various types of research and development cannot be clearly defined and, as a result, differences of opinion exist among individuals as to the classification of certain types of investigative endeavor. In general, research personnel are best qualified to decide the technical course of the investigative effort and the best classification of the program from the standpoint of the likely outcome.

Much of the fundamental research effort in the United States is performed by colleges, universities, and other nonprofit organizations. The federal government and industry have taken greater interest in fundamental research in the last few years with the realization that any lag in the generation of fundamental knowledge will retard advances in applied fields. The span of time required for the effect to be felt is growing shorter and shorter with the current rapid growth of advanced technological capabilities and the shrinking of the world through advances in travel and communications.

Applied research and, to an even greater extent, development have become increasingly important in industry and have received relatively enthusiastic support in recent years. To industrial managers, developmental effort is directly associated with a new product or more efficiency in production. Applied research is usually regarded as a necessary evil that must, in general, precede the development phase. Basic research, on the other hand, is not looked upon very favorably. For small companies this may be excusable; however, for large industries, which can afford to be leaders, such an attitude, to say the least, is short sighted.

Annual federal and company funding for research and development performed by industry amounts to over twenty billion dollars. Over half of this funding is provided by the government. The remaining funds, contributed by industry, amount to approximately 2 percent of the net sales realized by the companies performing this research and development.

The companies represented by the above statistics were of various sizes. Many small companies have achieved rewarding profits from modest and judicious research and development investments. Many more small companies could certainly benefit from similar approaches, especially if some government support for the research were made available. Even large companies, universities, government agencies, private research institutions, etc., can improve returns on their research and development investments. All that is required is good research organization, good personnel, wise investment in facilities, and realistic planning. In industry this planning must take cognizance of the fact that research should not be under the control of production. It should be a separate entity, subject of necessity to overall company or corporate control, but not subject to pressures for immediate results. The peculiar requirements of an effective research environment need to be understood and respected.

Chapter 2

Organization for Research and Development

IF A GROUP or an individual makes a decision to conduct research and development operations, a problem is posed regarding the appropriate organization to be established to obtain the desired objectives. The research organization decided upon may be the most important factor which will determine whether or not the original decision to support research and development was wise. However, before establishing a formal organization, many factors should be taken into consideration to assure the soundness of the decision to initiate the research and development effort. A few of the most important items to consider are given in the following questions:

1. What is the basis of the decision to do research and development?
2. Is the decision based on accurate market surveys?
3. How much money can safely be invested in research and development without danger to the supporting organization?
4. Who is available to do the work?

The decision to sponsor or conduct research and development may be based on many different reasons. In the case of the individual researcher, the purpose may be self-satisfaction coupled with the hope of financial gain. Individual inventors set up basement laboratories, sponsor experimentation out of their own savings, and, in some cases, come up with marketable and profitable products. Unfortunately, many would-be researchers lack the education and background for determining feasible avenues of investigation. They tackle problems in violation of one basic law: *You can't get something for nothing.* These individuals come up with perpetual motion machines and similar devices for which the impracticality has been established by the basic laws of science. A good example of a perpetual motion machine is the automobile which has one wheel geared to an air-compressor, while another wheel is geared to an air-motor to drive the vehicle. It is obvious to one trained in engineering that the work of compressing the air will exceed that available from expanding it through an air motor. Various losses enter into each process to cause this difference. Even for perfect processes, no net excess of energy would be available from the system to drive the automobile. Many other more sophisticated ideas, which are sometimes difficult to debunk, absorb large amounts of money and time of uneducated but dedicated individuals. If such activity does not absorb too much of the individual's income and time, it can be considered a recreation and is as useful as playing pool or golf or bowling. The pathetic case, however, is always present where the researcher mortgages his home and future earnings to support work which is basically unsound. But before the would-be inventor is criticized too much, consider the company which sometimes falls into the same trap.

Company X, a small, family-owned corporation which is building aluminum furniture is quite successful; however, its owners are bored with making "unglamorous" products. Inventor Y, who has created a three-dimensional tilting chair for rocket ships, comes to Company X with a proposition to build these chairs. Of course, some preliminary research work must be done before the chair is fully developed. The owners of Company X, having read about space and rocket ships in the newspapers and magazines are impressed. They are anxious to get into the space business. On the spur of the moment or perhaps with due deliberation based upon information furnished by the inventor, they decide to finance the chair development. One-hundred thousand dollars are authorized for the necessary research, and the fact that it has taken years to accumulate this capital is not even considered. The decision to spend the money is rationalized with visions of profits from the new business. One-hundred thousand dollars later, with the aluminum furniture business badly in need of capital and no orders for chairs for rocket ships, the investors are sadder and wiser. This example is somewhat analogous to that of the perpetual motion machine; both are based upon unsound information. *Small companies should not embark upon R and D excursions without accurate market surveys.*

Similar examples of research and development expenditures, which are based upon poorly conceived decisions, may also be found in large industries. However, with the advent of government support for research and development, uneconomical research efforts need not be too damaging to the corporation. In fact, in many cases, companies have benefited from these efforts because of cost reimbursement and fixed-fee types of contracts. The above leads us to another basic observation: *People are human and humans make mistakes.*

From the above it appears that errors in judgment will

occur if something is not done to minimize human frailties. Of course, whereas some individuals and companies will make serious errors in judgment, others will make advantageous decisions. Small companies with good managers will grow large by developing new products through the judicious use of research and development, and large corporations will grow larger.

Because present government spending contributes to such a large portion of the research and development effort in the country, the governmental attitude towards research furnishes the climate and will influence, to a large extent, how the money is spent. If a favorable attitude exists, then beneficial research will accrue because of the effort expended. If, however, the government specifies in detail or misdirects the research effort, then most of the effort will be expended on costly developmental projects and the more basic or fundamental research, the fountainhead from which new ideas and concepts flow, will suffer.

The total research effort of the country is a summation of all the efforts, small and large, of the various organizations doing research and development. Some firms may have excellent research groups and turn out much effective and creative work. Other firms may have poorer research capabilities and, consequently, will turn out a poorer product. On the average, however, the returns from the total research effort will depend largely on political and management decisions by the government and, to a lesser extent, by the large corporations which expend a portion of their sales dollar for company-sponsored research.

In the development of basic or fundamental concepts, a minimum of administrative control, which is the power to allocate funds for designated efforts, is desirable.

Freedom to follow new paths or avenues of research that open up should be extended to competent and able researchers. *What makes a competent and able researcher?* In general, it is possible to determine the worth of a man on a basis of past performance. Of course, young men just starting their careers may be handicapped in obtaining financial support for their ideas; however this may be a healthy situation in that it forces them to exert themselves more than they would if money were handed to them on a "silver platter."

In the case of applied research, administrative control must be applied in order to obtain a desired result within a reasonable period of time. Without the ability to control budgets and personnel, research administrators cannot prevent unreasonable delays. One case illustrates this point very vividly. A large research organization obtained a proposal request from a government agency for a piece of experimental apparatus. In accordance with their standard practice, they turned the request over to one of their employees for his consideration. After a thorough perusal of the proposal request, the employee discussed the work with the research administrator, and assured the research administrator that he could do the job in two months and for a few thousand dollars. The research administrator, realizing that nothing can be done for a few thousand dollars and in two months, tripled the estimates and submitted a proposal to the government for consideration. In due time a contract was negotiated, the employee was appointed to the post as project director, and the work started. Everything proceeded smoothly until one serious unexpected difficulty arose. The project director, being a perfectionist, kept building up the equipment and then tearing it down when he found a better way to do the job. This kept up until two years and twenty thousand dollars later the work was completed. Fortunately, the project director did such an excellent job that he received the plaudits of his sponsor; however, during the period of the research he nearly drove the administrators of the work at his institution and the government out of their minds. This points out another rule which is important in the management of research: *Never use brilliant idealists to direct applied or developmental research for which there are time and dollar limits.*

In regard to developmental research, the sponsor must exert close fiscal and time control over the work in order to obtain the item he wants when he wants it. Of course, picayunish details should be kept to a minimum.

The above briefly indicates the degree of administrative control necessary for the type of research being considered. However, to recapitulate:

1. Basic research should be as free from administrative details as possible in order to stimulate the free run of the mind of the researcher. This should result in the generation of many new concepts. Of course, some of the ideas will appear useless, but others will be good and one good idea can compensate for many useless ideas.

2. Applied research should be administered with a minimum of routine details in order to attain a desired result in a fixed time. Excessive administrative detail should be avoided because it de-emphasizes the technical effort.

3. Developmental research should be closely supervised from a fiscal and time standpoint in order to assure that the required equipment is available in the time limit set for the work. In the engineering systems being built today, it is not uncommon for several complex

components to be developed simultaneously. Without coordination and time schedules, the procurement of these mating subsystems would be a haphazard occurrence and completion of the engineering system in a reasonable period would be impossible.

The foregoing indicates that if fundamental researchers are closely supervised, then the number of basic ideas available may decline. It also indicates that applied and developmental researchers might procrastinate in doing their assigned tasks if they are not supervised. It implies that research and development projects have products which are as tangible as new automobiles. It also implies that in order to obtain good products from research and development work, hit or miss administrative organizations may be unsatisfactory. Consequently, it appears that to increase the probability of doing good research work, an administration designed to produce good research is essential.

Before forming too definite an opinion on research administration and its influence, it is desirable to look at the work of Donald C. Pelz (see references) who investigated the question "Is it true that the man who sets his own technical goals will perform better than one who is influenced by others?" In a five-year study of eleven organizations, he found that a technical man's performance is generally better when several "decision-making influences" are involved in setting his goals. Mr. Pelz also found that the autonomous scientist does not necessarily perform better than the man whose technical goals are determined by others. The most productive man appears to be one who has substantial control over his goals, but who is influenced by others. A deadly situation exists when the boss alone sets the goals.

Figure 2–1 indicates the percentile performance, as

measured by scientific contribution, papers published, and unpublished reports, for Ph.D.'s in developmental laboratories. In this case increasing administrative decision-influencing echelons improves performance in all three areas. Figure 2–2 indicates that Ph.D.'s in research

Ph.D.'s in Development Labs

For these Ph.D.'s, in labs where executives place higher value on development of better products than on addition to scientific knowledge, it appears that highest performance is achieved when four decision-making sources—or "echelons"—are involved in setting the scientists' technical goals.

FIG. 2–1

PERFORMANCE OF RESEACHERS IN DEVELOPMENT LABS AS A FUNC-
TION OF DECISION-MAKING INFLUENCES (AFTER PELZ)

laboratories improve their performance in all three areas after three levels of administrative decision-influencing control. It also indicates that they perform well on their own (one level) in scientific contributions. It should be noted that the figures are averages for one hundred Ph.D.'s and, consequently, mask out the influence of the highly creative individual.

Since World War II, the growth of research and development effort has created many organizations which are geared to solving problems, developing new concepts, and creating new product ideas. These organizations do not mass produce consumer goods. They do not have a production line unless it is one of technical reports. Also,

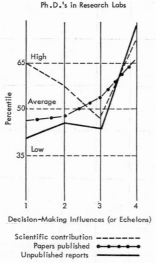

Of these Ph.D.'s, some 100 in all, about half work in government, the others in university departments. Publication of knowledge is more highly valued here than the creation of better products. Why do "one influence" people contribute more? Perhaps those autonomous Ph.D.'s talk more than they write.

FIG. 2–2

PERFORMANCE OF RESEACHERS IN RESEARCH LABS AS A FUNCTION OF DECISION-MAKING INFLUENCES (AFTER PELZ)

they have demonstrated their success by rapid growth. These organizations are described and discussed in the following pages.

The Nonprofit State Educational Research Organization

With the basic ingredients for doing research on their campuses, it is not surprising that many large universities both privately endowed and publicly controlled, have developed organizations for handling research and developmental type of work. Figure 2–3 shows the growth in

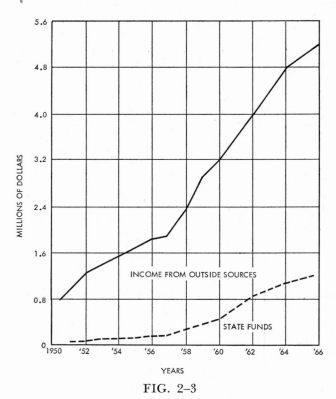

FIG. 2–3

GROWTH OF RESEARCH EXPENDITURES FOR A TYPICAL
UNIVERSITY RESEARCH OPERATION

dollar volume of research expenditures for a typical state institution of higher learning. This growth is illustrative of other similar organizations across the country. Of course, the order of magnitude of the ordinate will vary with location and school; however, the same general trends are indicated by many of the foremost engineering and science schools.

How do educational institutions get into research? In many cases, if support is derived from public funds, it is found that the vehicle is a legislative act establishing a research station for the institution. These acts may have been passed many years ago and, like a seed resting upon barren soil, have been kept dormant until the climate for research became favorable after World War II. For instance, one state legislature in 1919 passed an act establishing an engineering experiment station at its technological engineering school. The act reads in part *". . . it shall be the object and duty of the Experiment Station to conduct original researches, perform and verify experiments, and make investigations in any or all branches of engineering, and sciences related thereto, and to compile data relating to such researches, for the promotion of the interest of the people of the State."* With the legislative problems taken care of by far-sighted legislators of the past and, with a climate for research growth after World War II, it is not surprising that the growth of research in the United States has been rapid.

Although the main vehicle for handling research was already available on many campuses, still one ingredient for a successful operation was lacking. This lack was an organization, not politically controlled, to handle the contracts with governmental and industrial sponsors. Consequently, nonprofit corporations, usually called foundations, were often formed and closely integrated into the fabric of the educational institutions. These corporations handle contractual relations with external agencies in connection with the performance of research and development projects. They are not handicapped by complicated state regulations and are not subject to the whims of politics. Usually the governing board of the nonprofit corporation is composed of members selected from industry at large, the institution's faculty, and alumni foundation members. Extremely competent governing boards are easily obtained and may have been at least partially responsible for the many successful and outstanding educational research organizations.

The nonprofit foundation, as stated before, handles contractual matters with sponsors. In addition, it usually collects money for the work, reimburses the institution for expenditures, handles patent matters, and acts as a repository for accumulating funds. Many advantages besides these also accrue to the institution from the foundation. For instance, gift donors who might be reluctant to give funds to a state-supported institution feel free to give funds to the foundation to be used for the benefit of the school.

The research station, the nonprofit foundation, and the educational institution can be combined into three possible types of organization. In the first type the research station is set up as an integral unit with the responsibility for conducting research vested in full-time employees who have no obligations to academic departments. In this type of organization the nonprofit foundation is usually closely associated with the research station and the director of the station reports directly to a major administrative officer of the educational institution. Figure 2–4 shows an organizational chart for this type of structure. It should be noted from the figure that the administration of sponsored research, both governmental and industrial, is vested in personnel with no ties to academic departments. The use of academic personnel on the research projects as project directors, etc., is permitted. In addition, students both undergraduate and graduate, are permitted to work on projects as long as their doing so does not interfere with their academic programs. The students and staff alike benefit from the practical experience gained in performing the sponsored work. Also, the institution in turn obtains many benefits from the research programs; for instance, equipment, better staff, financially secure students, and last but not least an enhancement of reputation resulting from station publications and contacts with sponsoring agencies.

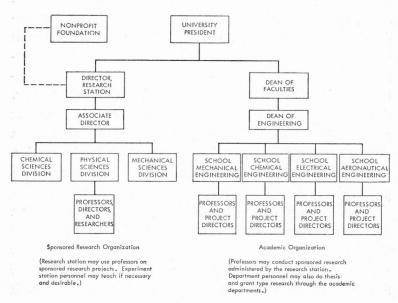

Sponsored Research Organization

(Research station may use professors on sponsored research projects. Experiment station personnel may teach if necessary and desirable.)

Academic Organization

(Professors may conduct sponsored research administered by the research station. Department personnel may also do thesis and grant type research through the academic departments.)

FIG. 2–4

Separation of Research and Academic Instruction

In many cases, these agencies are potential or active buyers of the university's product, the Bachelors, Masters, and Doctor of Philosophy graduates.

With the type of organization just described, it is still possible for research to be done in the academic departments. For instance, a professor may elect to conduct his project for the station in the departmental laboratories and to use his students as project engineers. Of course, the final administrative control of the work is vested in the research station and not in the academic department head. This schism of authority and responsibility, as could be expected, leads to trouble. Normally, as long as the research station's total salary amount is small compared with academic salaries and the institution's graduate program is small, no serious conflict results; however, as soon as the station's payroll and the number of graduate students become appreciable, then difficulties can be expected. These difficulties are evinced by academic criticism of the station's policies. At this time it would be more efficient for the research station to operate as a separate entity. Of course, the academic administrators, being human, will prevent this. In all probability, the station personnel will be placed more firmly under academic control. This action may tend to stifle for a short time the growth of the sponsored research activity. It may, however, be the best course for the institution to pursue in order to help fund its graduate programs.

A criterion is needed to indicate when the separation of the research station from the academic institution should take place. It appears to the authors that either separation or incorporation into the academic fabric of the institution should take place when the research station's effort approaches 25 percent of the total institution's budget.

Through academic control, the research effort is restored to its proper place as defined by the academicians. This then gives the second of the three type of organizations possible. Here the director of the research effort either reports to, or is himself, a dean or vice president for research. This type of organization is shown in Figure 2–5. Research is actually performed in the departments and the responsibility for research administration is vested in the department heads. If the available department heads are also experienced research managers, then the research will not suffer too drastically; however, it will probably become directed towards academically oriented projects with the large money-producers in applied and developmental research areas being ignored. This, of course, will tend to reduce the overall research budget of

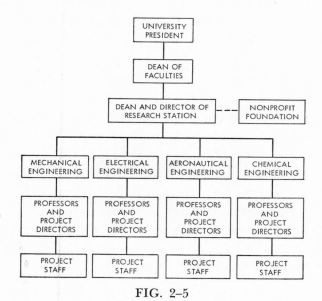

FIG. 2–5

EXAMPLE OF A COMBINED ACADEMIC AND
RESEARCH ORGANIZATION

the institution unless some way can be found to give the good applied research and development personnel some academic status. Here it is interesting to consider an amusing definition of basic or fundamental research as compared with applied or developmental research. This definition was provided by one of those rare individuals who values both the scientific and practical aspects of research. The definition which he says he and his colleagues apply to themselves is: "What I'm doing is basic or pure research; what anyone else is doing is applied or developmental research." This attitude is very prominent on many campuses.

In the third type of organization, as has been implied above, the academic institution is separated from the research organization. Control of research is now vested in the nonprofit corporation, and the academic institution has a part in this control in proportion to the number of staff members it has on the corporation's board of directors. This cleavage frees the research organization from restrictions on its growth. If the staff has not been damaged too much by the skirmishes prior to the separation, and if sufficient funds can be raised, it continues to grow in size in accordance with the research climate of the country and the ability of its top administrators. The third type of organization then takes its place with other nonprofit research organizations. However, in this type of organization the research program has little or no effect on the quality of the end product of the educational institution, its graduates.

The Private Educational Institution

In contrast with the state educational institution, the private educational institution is not hampered by ties to a state for financial support. Endowments, grants, active alumni contributions, tuition, and research contracts make up the majority of the funds available to this type of operation. The institution is usually a nonprofit corporation whose original purpose was education. During World War II the corporation utilized its academic staff to branch out into research and development endeavors. With the control of all the effort in the hands of strong administrators, the welding together of education and research was possible. The growth of research in this type of environment was extremely rapid and, in some cases, it soon surpassed the academic effort.

When the effort of the research station of a state institution is absorbed into its nonprofit corporation, an operation similar to that of the private institution becomes possible. In this case, the organization would at first be oriented towards research endeavors; however, nothing would prevent it, at a later date, from initiating an educational program into its activities. This process would be the reverse of the procedure by which the private educational institution became research oriented. It is an interesting process to contemplate.

The Nonprofit Research Organization

In some cases a nonprofit research organization may result from other than an academic background. For instance, a philanthropist may set up a research center out of his love for mankind. Irrespective of how the organization was created, its operation will drift into a "research for money" situation if it is to keep pace with other research groups in growth and reputation. Despite idealistic thoughts to the contrary, money, or what it can buy, is still the greatest stimulus for getting people to accomplish anything.

Another type of nonprofit organization, which has thus far not been mentioned, is the one established specifically for and by a branch of the federal government. The purpose of this organization is to furnish consulting and project management services for its sponsor. For instance, the Rand Corporation was sponsored by the Air Force to provide the Air Force with studies of advanced weapon systems, consulting advice, etc. Many excellent Rand reports are available and these reports are not as biased as they probably would be if they were written by personnel of the government. In fact, some of the reports are critical of various Air Force systems, personnel, and practices. The use of a nonprofit corporation in this manner by the services is an excellent idea and has several advantages. Specifically, the organization is separated from the civil service salary scale and government red tape, and it is able to pay the salaries necessary to attract the scientists required to make the type of analyses the far-sighted government administrators need.

The Private Profit Institution

Private organizations for exploiting research and development for profit have existed for many years. Prior to the end of World War II these organizations had to be extremely competent if they were to continue in business.

One of the advantages that a private organization has over an academic institution is that it has only one primary product. The academic institution doing research has two: graduates and research results. As could be expected, the academic institution usually prefers to concentrate on its students and to have research improve its main product. This situation does not permit rapid handling of research programs because of the requirements of classes, examinations, theses, etc. The fact that the private research organization needs a profit to survive usually means that its cost for a research job will be higher than that for the comparable academic organization; however, when time is critical, cost is not the governing item and singularity of purpose is important. One other advantage that private organizations may have is that their salary scales are not tied to an academic system. This permits them to reward competent researchers in a more flexible manner. Sometimes the most expensive ingredient in a research program is the poorly paid scientist or engineer. One good man is usually capable of producing more output than many mediocre researchers.

In addition to the research and development type of organization there are many independent laboratories in the country which are devoted primarily to testing. These companies perform a vital service to industry by certifying materials and equipment. They form a group of the nation's leading independent laboratories and promote scientific analysis, testing, and inspection. Of course, these laboratories are also interested in research and development and are not averse to taking work in the basic and applied sciences. Collectively, they employ thousands of chemists, engineers, physicists, metallurgists, biologists, and technicians. The work they do includes the development and improvement of products and processes, sampling and analysis of raw or partly finished products, control of quality of finished products, control of performance of personnel, and investigations into the nebulous regime of consumer appeal.

Despite all criticisms and plaudits of private profit organizations, one fact of primary importance is evident. These organizations are born, live, and die in the highly competitive market place wherein the incentive for performance is money. To obtain money, the customers must be pleased. Therefore, a successful laboratory is one which performs a necessary service well and for a price which is competitive. In addition, private corporations for profit must pay taxes. This is in contrast with the nonprofit organizations which enjoy a tax-free existence. Irrespective of the type of organization involved, the pertinent facts are that the availability of money and the type of men in the organization will determine whether or not the organization will survive in modern competitive society. This competition also affects the nonprofit organizations who depend to a large extent upon support from industry and government agencies.

The Government Research Organization

One type of research and development organization whose survival is not wholly dependent upon its competitive stature is the government laboratory. The government conducts research in the following areas: agriculture, aerial photography, Department of Defense problems, animal diseases and parasites, atomic energy, cartography, chemistry, child welfare, coal, aeronautics and space, dairy husbandry, dental, disarmament, disease, economics, education, fishery, forestry, geochemical, geologic and geophysical sciences, health, helium, highway construction, labor, marketing, medicine, meteorology, mineral resources, paleontology, photogrammetry, saline water conversion, soil, topographic surveying and mapping, water resources, weather, wildlife, and many others. It is obvious that the federal government runs an extensive research organization; which spent over three billion dollars in 1965. Government laboratories in this country have turned out excellent work. For instance, the former National Advisory Committee for Aeronautics, now the National Aeronautics and Space Administration, in its laboratories in Cleveland, Langley, Ames, etc., contributed significantly to the development of modern aviation. Without the basic information generated by the NACA, the aviation industry could not have made the rapid strides which have produced jet intercontinental aircraft.

Hard-headed business men may criticize the government laboratories for doing work which they feel themselves capable of handling. This criticism is not wholly justified. Much of the government research cannot satisfactorily be handled by private corporations because of the nature of the work. Imposing a businessman in the organization would just increase the cost to the taxpayer with no attendant benefit to the work. This does not mean that the government should do all of its research. Rather, it should concentrate its effort in areas which cannot be handled easily and profitably by industry. The man-on-the-moon project is a good example of a program of research and development which is too large for any one corporation or even a group of corporations to handle. This project requires the combined effort of the government, large corporations, small companies, and the taxpayers to make it succeed.

Company-Financed Research and Development Organizations

Company-financed R and D has as its major objective new and better products to meet competition and produce profits; therefore, research and development activities within a company are usually organized along product interest lines. For example, a diversified chemical company may be sponsoring research and development effort in plastics, agricultural products, detergents, industrial chemicals, and other similar areas. Each of these is a product area in which the company has a production interest. The more progressive firms also sponsor a limited fundamental research effort which, they believe, will shorten the lead time from the conception of an idea to the actual marketing of a product. The actual structure of the applied research groups varies from company to company. Many of these groups consist of a large number of separate project teams working in specific topic areas with very little administrative structure between them and the research manager. An organizational structure of this type is shown in Figure 2–6. Sharply contrasting with this "horizontal" structure is the "vertical" organization which is favored by some companies. This type of

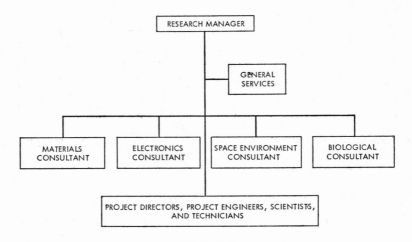

FIG. 2–6

ORGANIZATIONAL CHART WITH HORIZONTAL STRUCTURE

structure is shown in Figure 2–7. The horizontal organization provides greater freedom and flexibility for the research personnel, but requires that these people be extremely versatile in their creative abilities. The vertical structure actually consists of specialists who may work on several projects simultaneously, considering only the aspects which fall into their area of specialization. A project director in a vertical organization usually has much less control over the efforts of the individual project personnel since many of these people do not report directly to him. The fact that each specialist in a vertical structure must respond to the pressures applied by many groups breeds discontent and sometimes results in the loss of good engineers and scientists. A research manager must be a diplomat and minimize feelings of pressure and maximize a cooperative spirit in his organization.

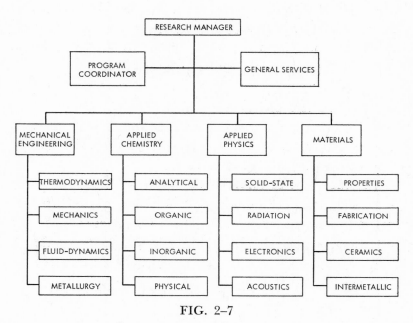

FIG. 2–7

ORGANIZATIONAL CHART WITH A VERTICAL STRUCTURE

Many small- and medium-sized companies usually have only a single development project under way at any one time. As a result, the company has a single group organized to handle all of its development projects. A group of this type is, therefore, project-oriented and composed of versatile engineers who are able to tackle virtually any developmental problem that may arise. An organizational structure of this type offers a challenge and diversification of duties to the team personnel.

Research and development in some companies may be a stepchild that has a precarious existence. Production comes first and research effort has sometimes been degraded to the role of quick fixes for various problems arising in production. This type of operation makes it extremely difficult to obtain creative work from the research organization.

Large corporations often set up separate research organizations which are separated from the parent company. By this means it is possible to create a good research atmosphere and a productive environment; even so, such a research division must be closely coordinated with the engineering, manufacturing, and sales activities of the company. Unfortunately, small companies cannot subsidize a large research group which does not contribute immediate profits.

Another type of research organization is the company research and development group which is partially subsidized by company funds but which runs these funds into a budget of several times the original amount by doing sponsored work for the government. This organization operates in the following manner. The company may authorize a budget of one million dollars per year for the establishment of a research group. The group when established utilizes the company funds to obtain competency in an area of interest to the government, and as a result is soon in a position to obtain government-sponsored work in the chosen area. Sponsorship is obtained from the government and the original one million dollars per year soon becomes several millions worth of research. The parent company benefits both financially and scientifically because of the original investment. Of course, it is assumed here that good personnel are available to administer such a program at its conception. This type of research is extremely valuable to a progressive company because it is essentially of the minimum-loss type. The company has available, as a result of a small investment, an outstanding research organization which can be drawn upon on short notice to help solve company problems. Competency in research will also help the company in obtaining development and production contracts and, last but not least, the results of the research work for the government can easily be incorporated into the company's commercial production. This type of organization then is one where loss is minimized and even unsuccessful research programs are not too costly. Unfortunately, the life expectancy of this type of operation is limited, since any profit squeeze results in curtailment of the company's funding.

Summary

In this chapter the nonprofit state educational research organization, the private educational institution, the nonprofit organization, the private profit organization, the government laboratory, and the company-financed laboratory have been discussed. From the many and varied types of organizations successfully doing research, it appears that each has its place. The question as to what is the ideal research organization is, therefore, difficult to answer. The survival of the many types over the years indicates that each must serve an important segment of the overall research and development requirement. It is apparent, however, that every good research organization must have certain elements if it is to survive. First, the organization must have creative, intelligent, and versatile scientists. Second, it must have an administration, environment, and tools for the implementation of creative ideas into reality. Third, it must operate in a climate which permits the organization to exploit the products of its creative research and development men. And fourth, it must make use of market surveys and information to assure that the results of its effort are worthwhile from a need and/or financial standpoint.

The ideal research and development organization, therefore, comprises men, environment, and opportunity. These three ingredients comprise almost any organization. The difference between the successful organization and the one which does not survive is in the selection of the type of men, the creation of a research environment, and the exploitation of the research opportunities which are available.

Chapter 3

Staffing the
Research and Development
Organization

IRRESPECTIVE of the type of research that is contemplated, be it basic, applied, or developmental, the success of the research effort will depend greatly upon the men and women making up the research organization. In many cases a good research staff is obtained only after much culling. Often good scientists or engineers have to be released from research and development activity because they lack the knack of inventing and correlating ideas into salable products for the research organization. They also lack the ability of working in areas about which little is known. In other activities, such as teaching and routine engineering, these men perform admirably. Hence, not all scientific and engineering personnel, and this is true at all educational levels, are suitable for research and development efforts. In fact, the number of research and development types is a very small proportion of the total technical manpower reservoir.

In view of the above, research managers must be aware of the various types of people who comprise the technical manpower pool. They must be able to select those types which offer the highest probability of creating new ideas and concepts, and who, at the same time, are capable of working without close supervision in fields where few facts are available. It is apparent, therefore, that the director of a research and development effort should be an outstanding and exceptional person. He must have one talent which is exceedingly rare. This is the ability of selecting, attracting, and retaining creative individuals. One industrial research manager stated, *"When people achieve positions of supervision over creative men and are themselves deficient in this quality—then an atmosphere develops which is deterring to idea men."* Consequently, it is apparent that creative people should be supervised or directed by creative people.

Closely associated with the selection of research personnel is the research budget. If sufficient funds are not available to support a competent research staff, it will probably be more advantageous to the parent company to contract the desired research work to some reputable research and development organization.

Another factor also closely associated with the selection of personnel is the type of project being undertaken. Research in chemistry, for instance, would require creative chemists while research in electronics would require creative physicists and electrical engineers.

The remainder of this chapter will cover the types of people who comprise the technical community; the types who have the greatest probability for high-yield contribution to various facets of research; the techniques for interviewing and recruiting prospective researchers; and the cost associated with the support of suitable researchers.

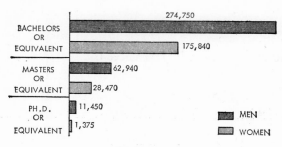

FIG. 3–1

<small>**DEGREES GRANTED BY INSTITUTIONS OF HIGHER LEARNING, 1963**</small>

Technical Manpower Reservoir

In the United States of America approximately two thousand institutions of higher education turn out a most priceless product, educated young people. Figure 3–1 gives the number of baccalaureate and higher degrees granted in 1963. From the annual recipients of college degrees come the intelligence and strength to sustain the large industrial and economic complex of the United States. As would be expected not all of the degrees are in the engineering sciences. In fact, less than

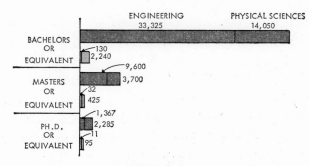

FIG. 3–2

<small>**ENGINEERING AND PHYSICAL SCIENCE DEGREES GRANTED IN 1963**</small>

half of the graduates possess the educational background which is today associated with engineering, research, and space science. Figure 3–2 indicates the number of various engineering and scientific degrees awarded in 1963.

The total number of engineers and scientists in private industry is indicated in Table 3–1 for the years 1959,

TABLE 3–1

ENGINEERS AND SCIENTISTS IN INDUSTRY

| | | Number | |
Occupational Group	1959	1960	1963
Engineers.	615,400	648,900	711,600
Chemists.	71,500	77,100	74,300
Physicists.	14,900	15,600	14,500
Metallurgists.	11,400	12,600	11,900
Geologists and geophysicists.	14,800	15,200	12,300
Mathematicians.	11,300	14,100	20,400
Medical scientists.	7,000	6,600	
Agricultural scientists.	5,600	5,900	18,400
Biological scientists.	5,500	7,300	
Other scientists and engineers.	6,700	9,400	8,000
Totals.	764,100	812,700	871,300

1960, and 1963. Although the 1963 data are not directly correlated with those of 1959 and 1960, the table indicates the increased need for engineers and mathematicians in industry. The large reservoir of technical and trained personnel is utilized by industry to produce the ideas and products necessary for its growth and continued existence. The division of engineers and scientists in industry in 1960 into research and development, management, and other roles is provided in Table 3–2.

From the above it is evident that large numbers of potential engineers and scientists are produced annually in the United States. These educated young people are as necessary to a technological machine as are the raw materials on which it feeds. Without them to provide a continuity of direction, the engineering and scientific leadership of the United States would be lost. Consequently, progressive corporations are continually recruiting young people for incorporation into their organizational structure.

TABLE 3–2

UTILIZATION OF ENGINEERS AND SCIENTISTS
IN VARIOUS INDUSTRIAL ROLES IN 1960

Occupational Group	Research and Development	Management and Administration	Production	Other
Engineers..............	190,400	92,200	268,800	97,500
Chemists...............	35,700	11,400	23,200	6,800
Physicists...............	12,300	1,900	900	500
Metallurgists...........	5,300	2,000	4,700	600
Geologists and geophysicists...........	600	1,000	1,600	12,000
Mathematicians..........	7,000	1,300	3,700	2,100
Medical scientists........	1,000	700	700	4,200
Agricultural scientists.....	1,100	1,100	1,900	1,800
Biological scientists.......	3,600	700	1,200	1,800
Totals............	257,000	112,300	306,700	127,300

Qualities of a Researcher

Although a large number of college graduates become available every year, it is not sufficient or prudent to assume that everyone will make a good researcher or even a good engineer. An additional ingredient is necessary. This vital ingredient for success in a creative career is curiosity. A supervisor for a large corporation once stated that he had no trouble obtaining engineers. His trouble was getting engineers who had initiative and who could think creatively. One of his major complaints was that, after an engineer had completed a designated assignment he would come running to the supervisor and ask what he should do next. In other words, the engineer could adequately complete a detailed assignment but he did not have the initiative, curiosity, and drive to determine what should be done next. He required the supervisor to detail all of his actions. The supervisor stated that he could walk through the plant and see a multitude of tasks that required action. Of course, this is one reason why he was the supervisor and not just one of the routine engineers. It may, however, be dangerous for the engineer to go off on his own and do something. He can, nevertheless, point out what he believes should be done and how he would propose doing it, thereby reducing his supervisor's load. This would be to his benefit in the long run since the ability to see what has to be done and determine how to accomplish it is usually well rewarded.

The discussion above introduces a facet of the problem of getting things accomplished. It is best illustrated by a study of the types of individuals available for industrial positions. The types are broken down into the following categories:

1. Intelligent and lazy
2. Intelligent and industrious
3. Stupid and lazy
4. Stupid and industrious

A decision is to be made as to the type of man to be selected for the position of general manager. This position requires decision-making ability and the ability to delegate responsibility and authority. It is obvious that the type of person required is identified by the first category, the intelligent and lazy individual. Being intelligent the man will be able to make good decisions. Intelligence will also minimize the chances of the man doing nothing and his laziness will help him delegate responsibility and authority. Although it may not appear to be difficult, the delegation of power, next to the proper selection of personnel, is the most difficult task of the manager. The type of men to use for the staff functions in the business is obviously the intelligent and industrious. Therefore the second category furnishes the staff for the general manager. Persons in the other two categories have no place in a progressive organization. The stupid-and-lazy individual may be used because he will do only what he is told. The stupid-and-industrious individual, however, will do what he is told and, in addition, other things which will tend to disrupt the best of organizations. Therefore, the last type is to be avoided. In the case mentioned where the manager was complaining about people not seeing what has to be done, it is tacitly assumed that the engineers involved were intelligent. They may have been intelligent-and-lazy; however, in all probability they were somewhere in the middle, i.e., partially intelligent and somewhat lazy.

The differences between various individuals can also be pointed out in another way. In any large organization many new personnel are added yearly. It is quite interesting to note how rapidly some individuals acquire an insight into what is going on throughout the organization, while others may have been at a place for several years and may still be ignorant of what is going on in the laboratories or offices next to them. This may seem to be ridiculous; nevertheless, a close scrutiny of any organization will reveal that it is true.

What makes a good researcher? The important ingredients can be generalized. A good researcher is a man who has a persistent inquisitiveness and curiosity about things and has an urge to improve everything he undertakes. He should have a good education and above-average intelligence. He need not be a genius; however, it is essential that his intelligence level be well above average. If this is not the case, he might cause his organization trouble through misdirected industriousness. Laziness, a characteristic of a good general manager, is not a characteristic which is helpful to a good researcher. Many successful scientists agree with Thomas Edison who attributed success to 90 percent perspiration and 10 percent inspiration. Inspiration, as defined here, is the ability to utilize the results of much labor in a manner that will produce a practical idea or useful product. The information Einstein used to determine his theory of relativity was available before his time. By using it, and probably after much hard work, he came upon ideas which he had the intelligence to evaluate and put into logical mathematical form.

How does one acquire inquisitiveness? It is doubtful if this characteristic can be acquired in a manner by which one would acquire the knowledge of differential equations. One is probably born with it and, as such, it shows up at a young age. Babies are usually very inquisitive. This type of inquisitiveness, however, is normal and not the type which is meant here. The inquisitiveness under consideration concerns the reasons why or how things work, rather than what they do. Most people are content if they understand the purpose of an item. For instance, many men and women operate automobiles, but only a few know even meager details concerning the operation of an internal combustion engine. They are inquisitive until they learn what they need to know to operate the automobile; beyond this point their inquisitiveness ends. A good researcher is always inquisitive. He never stops being inquisitive.

Another ingredient of a good researcher is creativity. As in the case of inquisitiveness, it is doubtful if this characteristic can be acquired by educational means. One appears to be born with it and again it shows up at a comparatively early age. Youngsters who invent novel toys and ways of doing things are creative. A good researcher can probably point to his past and illustrate how as a child he built novel gadgets. Many articles have been written on creativity and how to acquire it. These articles point out interesting procedures for encouraging and bringing forth latent creative talent. They also indicate that, in all probability, creative thinkers are born and not made. They point out that training may help develop latent creative ability; however, they also state that despite much training many individuals are creatively sterile. In essence, they indicate that creativity is a rare gift and that the most an analyst of creativity can do is point out the traits of a creative individual.

The creative individual must have a store of knowledge and must be continually engaged in enlarging his educational background; he must be industrious; he must have a sincere urge to accomplish something; he must be enthusiastic; he must have an inquiring mind; and, he must have a good imagination.

To select good researchers one must know how to evaluate them. The foregoing paragraph indicated six traits which should be considered when evaluating an individual for a research position. The first item is readily determined. The individual's credentials, transcripts from accredited colleges, and indications of his future educational plans are easily secured. They indicate the type of educational background to which the individual has been exposed and which he hopes to continue. The transcripts also indicate the relative success he had in competing with his contemporaries. Good grades indicate that he was successful in vying for competence with others in his classes. If little else is available on which to make a decision, then the individual's grades should be closely scrutinized. Of course, the relative standing of various universities should also be considered. It is not uncommon for failures at prominent universities to become successful students in the less competitive environment of a smaller or less difficult college.

Ability for self-education can partially be determined by past performance in obtaining advanced degrees and writing dissertations. A burning desire for an education will usually show itself in advanced degrees. The dissertations will to a large extent indicate ability for acquiring information which is not readily available. In addition they will indicate an industriousness and devotion to education. The topic of a dissertation may, in some cases, indicate an inquiring and analytical mind. The manner in which the work was handled will, in all probability, indicate how good an imagination the researcher possesses.

If research reports or publications by the applicant are available, they too should be scrutinized to determine whether or not their writer, the researcher under consideration, is satisfactory for the position for which he is being considered. Many individuals have limited interests and such individuals should be channeled into positions which will make the most of their capabilities.

In view of the above, it is evident that the researcher who will probably produce the greatest yield will be one who has the following attributes:

1. A good education and background in the disciplines covering the areas of research which are under consideration;

nced degrees in the field of interest;

ge to accomplish something and an inquisitive
s indicated by dissertations and publications in
of interest; and

m and a creative mind as indicated by pub-
s and results—patents may also be considered
of creativity; however, the background of
laims should be investigated carefully.

Interviewing

blem which currently impairs the
entific personnel recruiting efforts of
articularly larger ones, is the poor
often takes place between prospec-
l field interviewers. This problem
terviewers are not research oriented.
ing officials are interviewing a pro-
they often are unable to describe to
as of research in which the company
ther, they are unable to understand
ween the interests and experience of
he requirements of their company.
nate situation arises when the inter-
ugh comprehension of the company's
lopment program to be dangerous.
he erroneously believes he under-
hat is going on and assumes that he
dge the types of persons who would
quirements of the programs. It was
hat creative persons are best adminis-
dividuals, and it is also possible that
reened and selected by creative indi-
interviewers of prospective research

and development personnel should themselves be familiar with research and development problems and requirements.

The know-it-all recruiter usually results when the company sponsors a seminar or training program to acquaint personnel officers with the research and development effort. Selected research and development staff members—usually administrators who do not totally comprehend the details of the effort—deliver highly diluted and oversimplified summaries of the various programs in an effort to impress rather than educate the personnel officers. The product of this well-meant but misdirected training program is a less-than-half-informed "technical personnel officer" with a superior attitude that includes contempt for the efforts of the research and development program which he now feels are so simple that even he could serve in the bulk of the positions that are open. His attitude is usually conveyed through the interview discussion to the prospective technical employee. This attitude is interpreted by the prospect as representative of the overall company management philosophy with respect to research and development and, if the prospect is a potential researcher, he will probably not even accept an opportunity to visit the company's facilities. Many good contacts are lost in this manner.

In progressive companies which have successful recruiting programs, field interviewing is the responsibility of top research and development staff members. In the final analysis, the project leader or director himself is the only person who knows the type of people he needs to conduct his research programs. As a result, recruitment responsibility should not be allowed to drift too far from the shoulders of those who are best qualified to evaluate prospective new talent. The responsibility for field interviewing can be rotated among the various research and development staff administrators and project leaders so that the burden does not become too great for any single individual.

The use of research and development staff members as field interviewers and recruiters is often impossible. A shortage of good staff members as well as staff responsibilities which preempt any additional imposition, such as recruiting duty, contribute to this dilemma. Fairly recent graduates, engaged in research, are helpful in interesting people with potential value as researchers, particularly if they are sent to recruit at their Alma Maters.

A less satisfactory method of field contact, which nevertheless is often successful, involves the distribution of descriptive brochures among prospects by a company personnel representative. Insofar as contacting research and development prospects is concerned, the representative merely distributes the brochures which outline areas of current company R and D interest and activity. He may also provide interested persons with general information regarding facilities, company organizational structure, and historical facts. Care should be exercised to assure that the brochures are current and as explicit as possible in the details regarding the types of personnel required, description of duties, opportunities for professional development, professional stimulus, and company research and development philosophies. The proprietary nature of most company research and development activities imposes limitations upon the extent to which specific details can be provided; however, this does not prevent the inclusion of specific and accurate descriptions of background, experience, interest and other qualifications expected of persons needed to fill the various available positions.

In addition to company brochures, application forms should be provided to persons who feel that their interests and talents coincide with those outlined in the brochures. It is very important that the information requested on application forms be sufficient to provide research managers with an accurate basis for preliminary evaluation of applicants. In addition to the usual data (name, address, birth date and place, description, etc.) , information should be requested that will indicate the level of possession of the four attributes listed at the end of the preceding section of this chapter. To accomplish this, the application form should require:

1. Specific information in regard to education, experience, and training—grade transcripts should be required for men with limited background and experience;
2. Specific and detailed information in regard to advanced degrees;
3. Specific information, titles, and abstracts of dissertations and publications in the area of interest for which the applicant is being considered; and,
4. Specific and detailed information regarding patents and other items indicating creativity.

In the case of items 3 and 4, titles alone are not indicative of the level of achievement and it is desirable, in many cases, for the potential employers to secure copies of the articles and patents listed by the applicant. It does not seem inappropriate to require the applicant to supply, on a loan basis, copies of his most important publications. In addition to the items listed above, companies engaged in classified federal research and development programs should request information regarding the security clearance of the applicant or his ability to obtain a clearance.

Applications received by the company should be evaluated both by the project leader and the research manager to determine preliminary suitability. A careful and judicious screening of applications will result in an optimization of the number of invitations extended to applicants to visit the company facilities. Invitations should be extended only to those applicants whose backgrounds indicate promising coincidence of training, interest, and experience with the company or institutional requirements. The final decision of whether or not to make the applicant an offer is usually confirmed by a single visit with the research and development staff; however, in some instances, it is desirable that an applicant visit with the staff on a second occasion. This is particularly true in cases where the interview during the first visit indicated either sufficiently outstanding qualifications or interest and abilities on the part of the applicant in areas which are different from those of current importance to the organization. If the applicant is particularly outstanding he should probably be considered for a higher position than the one for which he was originally interviewed. If the applicant's areas of interest are diverse from those in which needs exist, he should be investigated further in order to determine whether or not he would be satisfactory for other positions for which he was not considered. It may be that upon further consideration a more suitable position can be found or created for the outstanding applicant which will still conform to the company's research program. Utilizing personnel below their capabilities and in positions in which they have no interest is fruitless and, consequently, uneconomical.

Some organizations obtain very successful results by including a "trial by fire" phase in the interview visit. In this phase, which usually takes place towards the end of the visit, an applicant for a position as a project leader or higher is requested to make a presentation on his fields of interest or research before a group of company staff members. The presentation usually terminates with a question and answer period. Any applicant who survives this ordeal probably has what it takes to manage one or more research projects. He at least has the ability to think on his feet and to convey his ideas to a group of his contemporaries. During the presentation, the applicant also gets the chance to evaluate the company staff, particularly from the questions they ask. This type of interview, in all probability, is beneficial to both parties since it minimizes misconceptions. The applicant knows the company and the company's representatives know the applicant.

In highly competitive areas of research and development, two possibilities for obtaining competent staff present themselves. These methods are simply described by two words—*stealing and growing.* Probably the better of the two methods is that of growing talent in the parent organization. This system requires a good recruiting program at the lower levels to continually supplement and replace personnel. When high-grade, intelligent, and ambitious young men are available, they will rapidly grow into competent and able researchers if given the opportunity. This opportunity may exist in various forms. For instance, a company-sponsored graduate program is most essential if good men are to be developed and retained. Other highly educated young men may require the opportunity of working closely with senior men of reputation. Some companies periodically hold seminars conducted by highly respected educators and scientists. Young men are encouraged to develop professionally in progressive organizations. The old philosophy that defined professional development as a *postgraduate enrichment in company policy* is passé.

One of the raiding grounds for company recruiters looking for competent scientists is the university campus. It is true that this is a rich preserve of scientific talent; however, in the long haul, those who steal professors and researchers from college campuses may find that future recruitment, even of bachelor candidates, is difficult. Also, many university professors do not readily adapt to industrial type operations. Occasionally unsolicited inquiries from professors and other college staff members will be received. If this happens, it may be to the benefit of the company to consider the possibility of obtaining these persons for technical employment. Under no circumstances, however, should company recruiters alienate the college community through imprudent tactics of any kind. They should remember that the universities create one of their most vital raw materials and that this supply is sensitive to advice and counsel provided by university officials.

Cost of Maintaining a Researcher

In determining the cost of maintaining a researcher, dollars should not be the only criterion of evaluation. Many hidden factors, to which dollar values cannot be assigned, affect the productivity and, consequently, the value of the researcher to an organization. Management must understand the expectations, goals, and even misconceptions of the scientist or researcher if it is to optimize its research capabilities. Therefore, management and engineering must resolve their mutual frustrations with each other if maximum contributions are to be made by each for the benefit of the whole organization.

In the past the traditional approach of management to attract good personnel was the liberal use of dollars. Ample moving allowances, bonuses, high starting salaries and special indoctrination trips were used and are still being used effectively. Nevertheless, despite the lucrative opportunities being proffered to new engineers and the relatively high salaries currently being paid to competent experienced engineers, symptoms of unrest among technical professionals still exist. Perhaps unrest is typical of a researcher; he is never satisfied. Perhaps the problem is not salaries, benefits, and working conditions, but rather a more fundamental one of end objectives. Management is required to make a profit; research on the other hand while not adverse to producing profit is more interested in understanding physical phenomena. As a consequence, engineers and scientists believe that management makes unrealistic demands on their time and effort. They desire a status and freedom from work pressure that are more appropriate to—at least so they think—a university. In many cases, they do not realize that universities in their current research boom are also beset with time limitations, budget controls, etc. It should be readily apparent that only the most successful and progressive corporations can afford the luxury of an ideal university atmosphere for their researchers.

Some scientists and researchers also fail to grasp management problems. Management, for instance, must take an occasional risk in making decisions. Most researchers prefer to be methodical and do a thorough and scientific job on any task they undertake. In some cases this may mean that a product will never be produced since it is not perfect. Management must draw some limit to such activities so that products, sometimes not perfect, can be placed on the market to at least partially satisfy a current need.

Another gap between engineering and management is the lack of appreciation of each group for the other's contribution to the success of the company. Each group tends to evaluate the other's accomplishments by its own standards. This is extremely dangerous and leads to much misunderstanding. It should be emphasized here that without the vast production and distribution system that management has built up, even the best research would be of little value. For instance, the development of the theory for supersonic flight would have been of little value in the nineteenth century. The technological status of the country at that time was not ready for supersonic flight. Of course, a futuristic novel could have resulted from the work. In like manner what good is a vast technological capability if nothing is fed into its pipeline. Engineering and management are, therefore, necessary to each other. Despite the necessity it is hard to convince scientists and engineers that they are not the king pins in our technology.

Because management controls budgets, etc., it also sets the rewards and determines the task assignments in any company. Therefore, unless management is extraordinarily wise, the only recourse for the researcher, if he desires to become a member of the affluent society, is to become a manager. In many cases engineers do enter management; however, for a good researcher this may mean giving up a way of life which can be very challenging and satisfying.

If the engineer decides to stay in engineering and research, he forever afterwards feels that he and his fellows are making the greatest contribution to the company, but that management gets the rewards and recognition. To be successful in manipulating engineers, management must somehow minimize the effects of this attitude on the part of its engineers and researchers. Efforts to do this are one cost of maintaining a researcher. This cost need not be in dollars but in the attitude and treatment of the engineers by other types of personnel in the company. Preferential treatment in regard to parking, vacations, working conditions, etc., in some cases may be as important as monetary rewards.

Another force, not mentioned before, that breeds discontent is the technical man's belief that he is a professional man. He often overlooks basic differences between self-employed professionals and employee-professionals, and would like the advantages of both types of operation without the disadvantages of either. For illustration, the employee-professional has equipment and capital furnished by management, has paycheck security, has regular hours, and must meet his boss' requirements. In contrast, the self-employed professional must provide his own equipment, has a salary dependent on fees, has self-determined work habits, and is responsible to himself.

A difficulty management faces is the shortage of good researchers which makes it necessary to cater to their desires and attempt to furnish them an atmosphere which is as near as possible, in desirable attributes, to that of the self-employed professional as well as that of the employee-professional. To do this, of course, increases the cost of maintaining a researcher.

Another price required of management is the toleration of the engineer's and researcher's self-image of genius. This image causes real trouble because it says to the engineer that he should only be working on *impor-*

tant new ideas. In other words every good researcher or engineer subconsciously wants to become another genius like Einstein, Newton, etc. Although management needs geniuses, many of the problems which must be solved are commonplace. This does not mean that they are unimportant, but simply that they are not glamorous. A common complaint of engineers, therefore, is that although they are keenly interested in new knowledge and developing new ideas, management just won't listen to their good ideas. On close examination, most of these so-called "good ideas" are not outstanding. If they do have scientific merit, in all probability, some other factor such as economy of production, etc., may make them impractical. If properly presented, good ideas will receive a hearing. If the researcher is unable to sell his idea, then either of two things is at fault: one, the idea is not very praiseworthy; or two, the researcher is a poor salesman and inept at presenting his thoughts. If the latter is the case, the researcher should take stock of himself and institute a course of self-improvement. An engineer who cannot properly present his ideas will have limited success even if he is a genius. Management, despite what was said above, should take some action to consider and evaluate the ideas of its research staff. An incentive program for good thinking may be a wise investment. This then is another cost of maintaining a good research organization.

Placing an actual dollar value on the expense of supporting a researcher is difficult. If the company has modern sophisticated facilities and equipment and has an extensive benefit program, if it has a university-type environment for its researchers, and if it has a good personnel program, then, in all probability, the cost per researcher will run between thirty to fifty thousand dollars per year. Other companies with less elaborate facilities and benefits may fund a researcher at twenty-five thousand dollars per year. Table 3–3 indicates research and development cost per R and D scientist or

TABLE 3–3

Cost per R and D Scientist or Engineer by Industry and
Size of Company, 1959–61
(Dollars)

Distribution by Industry	1961	1960	1959
Chemical processes................31,900		29,900	28,400
Electrical and electronics.............33,300		34,900	37,200
Petroleum refining and extraction......33,300		32,900	32,900
Aerospace.......................44,300		44,500	43,500
Machinery.......................29,100		30,600	31,500
Primary metals...................29,900		29,500	27,700
Automotive and transportation equip-			
ment..........................40,800		46,400	48,600
Food and kindred products...........19,200		19,200	17,100
Textiles and apparel................27,700		30,500	25,000
Lumber, wood products, and furniture. .25,800		24,600	20,000
Rubber products...................25,400		24,800	25,600
Fabricated metal products...........23,100		25,300	23,600
Other manufacturing industries.......25,000		25,000	25,300
Distribution by Size of Company *Based on Number of Employees*			
Less than 1,000.................... avg.		18,500	
1,000 to 4,999.................... avg.		26,000	
5,000 or more.................... avg.		38,000	

engineer, by industry and size of company. In this table the cost per R and D scientist or engineer was obtained by dividing total R and D performance funds (both federally and company-financed) by the average full-time equivalent of scientists and engineers engaged in research and development. It should be evident from these figures that research is not inexpensive and small companies should be extremely careful before they embark on a *research binge.*

Summary

The purpose of this chapter is to provide an understanding of the factors associated with the staffing of a research and development organization. These factors include (1) the types of people available for technical positions, (2) the types of people best suited for research and development, (3) recruitment of research and development personnel, and (4) the cost of maintaining a research and development staff.

A research and development organization is only as capable as the staff from which it is made. Not all technically trained personnel are qualified to do research and development work. A researcher must be able to perform original and creative endeavor in fields where little previous work has been done. An engineer or scientist may be extremely capable in routine engineering or scientific work which does not require originality and creativity. Despite other capabilities, a research organization staffed with people who are not creative is sterile.

Successful recruitment of research and development personnel requires maximum contact between these people and the research managers or project directors for whom they will work. The job application form cannot provide all the information necessary for the proper evaluation of a researcher. Further, the direct contacts will minimize the development of misconceptions by the prospective employee as well as by the employer. Well-prepared company brochures may help to explain research objectives, organizational structure, investigative areas, etc. During interviews it is worthwhile to provide opportunities for the prospective employee to express his ideas and interests before research staff members. This makes evaluation easier. Finally, companies should strive to maintain the best possible relationships with colleges and universities since these institutions are the fountainheads from which technical manpower originates.

The cost associated with the retention and maintenance of a research and development staff is influenced by many factors. By nature, most researchers are solo performers and behave like operatic prima donnas. They are inclined to be oriented towards research objectives which do not necessarily coincide with the commercial objectives of management. It is important that maximum opportunity be provided for the expression of new ideas to management by the research staff. Conversely, management clearly and comprehensively should point out its problems to the research staff. Through this exchange the researchers will eventually develop the ability to evaluate the practical worth of their ideas and themselves in terms of company objectives.

It is unrealistic for a company with limited surplus funds to entertain hopes of establishing an extensive research and development organization unless external funding is guaranteed. The reason for this is that the company will not be able to remain in business long enough to accrue any possible benefits from the research and development effort.

Chapter 4

Orienting
the Research Program

RESEARCH AND DEVELOPMENT efforts are expensive;
therefore, the industrial manager should orient his research and development effort into channels which will
offer compounded benefits to his company's overall operation. Because many large research and development
contracts are financed by the federal government, it is
interesting to note the experience of firms which have
tried to take the road of government R and D contracts to
obtain corporate profits. Disappointed industrial managers, when totaling up the return on capital and personal
investment, sometimes feel that their companies would
have benefited more if equivalent funds had been invested in stocks or bonds or even placed in commercial
banks. One of the difficulties encountered on government research and development contracts is the technical
proposal procedure, which is costly in time and dollars
and often yields relatively low returns in terms of contracts. It is not uncommon for nine, ten, or even more
companies to bid against each other on a specific research
effort.

Another difficulty is that of protecting the company's

proprietary position. If government research is undertaken with the hope of furthering corporate objectives, it is assumed that patent rights to inventions coming from the research will be retained by the company. This is not always possible and, consequently, contracts with government agencies, which take complete title to patents developed on the work cannot be justified.

The instability of an organization operating on government contracts is still another difficulty which makes the establishment of a productive research and development organization a Herculean task.

Despite these problems many companies with large defense production operations feel that Department of Defense research work is attractive from a business standpoint. They appreciate the advantage which is obtained from a reputation as a leader in scientifically oriented military research. They also benefit if they can retain civilian patent rights on their R and D military results.

It is apparent from current indications that R and D spending in the Department of Defense, the National Aeronautics and Space Administration, the National Science Foundation, and many other government agencies will continue to increase in the future. Therefore, a firm which is oriented towards the defense effort should embark upon a research program and develop a competent research staff which can successfully furnish ideas and products for exploitation in the defense and space areas. However, the illustration of the small manufacturer who wanted to develop space chairs and the research effort which strained the resources of his small company should be kept in mind even by large, well-financed corporations. If care is not taken they, too, can become financially embarrassed by unwise management decisions regarding research and development endeavor.

Orientation of the research program should begin with a careful analysis of the desired end objectives of the effort. It should also take into consideration the current capabilities of the company and the company's plans for growth in the future. If progressive management is available, the research and development growth capabilities of the corporation can at least parallel the coming rise in government research and development spending. Although, in many cases, the direct profit from a large research and development operation will be small, the intangible benefits may be appreciable.

Top management when investigating the feasibility of establishing a research and development operation should consider the following: (1) the primary purpose of the company or institution; (2) the type of problem or problems to be studied; (3) the relative value of the research program to the overall objectives of the company; (4) the availability of funds and facilities to support the research and development effort until federal or other sponsorship is obtained; and, (5) the personnel available to initiate the program.

After a research and development operation has been established it should generate a continuous flow of new ideas for possible research effort. Many of these ideas will be worthless from a financial standpoint; however, if the research effort is productive, there will also be valuable concepts which, if developed into consumer products, would accrue monetary benefits to the parent company. Therefore, associated with each of the new ideas is an accompanying question *Should this idea be supported?* Before embarking on a new research and development project, which is usually the development of an idea or concept, it is customary for management to make the *go* or *no-go* decision on the basis of data on market and economic potentials, available manpower, available funds, available facilities, and the possible chances for success. Obviously, for each new research venture facts are difficult to obtain and, in many cases, personal feelings and intuition take their places. Here the value of a good administrator becomes important. He will have an intuition, probably based on a wealth of experience with people and their capabilities, about those ventures that have the greatest probability for success. He will also have a built-in warning system which signals when unsound ideas and plans are presented. This is one reason why good managers are in demand and why they are paid handsomely in salaries, bonuses, stock options, and so on.

After a research and development program has been approved, it is the responsibility of the direct management echelons to determine the manner in which the company's money, men, and facilities are utilized to obtain the overall objectives set by top management. Here it is interesting to point out that the accomplishment of almost any objective requires three things: men, materials, and time. The men furnish ideas, plan the work, and manipulate the materials to obtain the finished product or goal. The time furnishes the boundaries for the completion of the work. It is self-evident that men and materials can be associated with dollars. A man costs a certain amount per year; a new lathe also has a price tag. This indicates, assuming the ready availability of men and materials, that in reality only two items are required to obtain an objective: money and time. Of course, the selection of the objective must be made judiciously and must consider the types of talent available and the technological capabilities of the community. For instance, it would be unwise to embark on an outer-space exploration program if the only men available were aborigines and the technological capabilities of the community could be classified as modern stone age. Such a program would be doomed from the beginning and would be wasteful of resources and fraught with disappointment.

If, however, one considers an advanced technological civilization such as the United States, then it is not inconceivable that by spending sufficient money a manned expedition to the moon can be successfully achieved. Materials, material fabrication methods, a reservoir of technically trained men, and an organized industrial complex are all available for utilization to obtain the desired goal. In this environment, money and time have interdependent meaning. If sufficient money is available then the industrial might of the nation can be focused on a particular project as it is now concentrated, through the National Aeronautics and Space Administration, on the conquest of space. Within limits, by spending more dollars the time period required to attain a specific goal can be shortened. Many factors, however, determine what the optimum time and optimum rate of expenditure should be. Too much spending may financially injure the country as it breaks a small company which injudiciously overextends itself. Too little could easily jeopardize the security and safety of the nation.

As stated in the foregoing, top management makes the initial decisions as to whether or not research and development will be undertaken and in what general areas the effort will be concentrated. In addition, top management will originally allocate funds, manpower, and capital equipment for this effort. After the broad outline or charter for the R and D effort has been obtained, it will be the responsibility of the research manager to see that the program gets implemented and oriented in the most efficient manner for achieving the goals set by the top management. Many types of organization are possible; some have been described in Chapter 2. However, the success of any research effort will finally be determined by the caliber of the men available to actually do the work. The technical project director, if he is an able leader, and if he has a relatively free hand to run his own program, will soon show profitable results from his efforts. It is, therefore, imperative for the research manager to select able and efficient project directors if he wishes to be the administrator of a successful research effort.

Initial Considerations

The type of research and development effort that will be established will, to a large extent, depend on the purpose and method of funding. If the purpose of the organization is to develop new products and supplement the operating divisions of a company, then the R and D effort will be supported primarily by internal company funds. If the purpose of the organization is to perform basic research which will enable the company to become a leader in its industry, then the support will probably be from company funds, supplemented by government contracts. Private universities and large nonprofit research organizations will be funded from gifts, endowments, government contracts, industrial contracts, and grants. State universities will be funded from the foregoing plus, to some extent, state funds allocated for research efforts. In the case of state universities, the state support may be a major portion of the research budget; however, in the most aggressive organizations, federal support of research and development makes up the major portion of the research budget.

Any research manager worth his salt is anxious to secure profits for his organization. Since the government expenditures in R and D total many billions of dollars, many able managers believe it is important to try for a slice of this huge sum of money and the attendant profits. Even though the agencies of the federal government will consider any idea which is submitted to them, an organization cannot simply submit ideas and start reaping profits. If an organization is to obtain and successfully fulfill research and development contracts for the government, it must have a technically competent research and development staff, proper facilities, and a feasible proposal or product. Before seeking external research and development support, the company should determine the answers to the following questions:

1. Is the research and development effort in an area in which the company has a proven capability?
2. Is the project important enough to the overall aims of the company to divert manpower and capital from other activities to perform the work?
3. Does the capability of the company and its research resources offer a fair chance of getting the desired research and development work funded?

In regard to the third question, the proposal procedure must be kept in mind. Proposal preparation is expensive, and proposal writing must be kept to a reasonable level. In addition, proposals should not be submitted for research which will strain the efforts of the company's staff to give even marginal or unsatisfactory results. This type of effort will result in damage to the company's reputation.

Selling research and development to government and industry is a competitive operation. In some cases, the competition may be extreme. For instance, a research request was sent from a federal government contractor to several potential subcontractor organizations for consideration. One organization, on reviewing the specifications and requirements of the purchase request, decided that these limitations were too severe for the end results desired. In other words, the specifications and requirements, if adhered to, would generate an extremely expensive research and development program, the results of which would be no better than those that could be obtained by utilizing a reduced set of requirements. Accordingly, a proposal was submitted which was based upon and specified the new set of requirements. This proposal had a dollar value of approximately one-third of that which would have been required to satisfy the initial conditions in the purchase request. The proposal was submitted to the sponsor and, in due time, a new request for a proposal based upon the revised specifications was received. Upon resubmitting the original proposal, which caused and satisfied the new set of requirements, and after waiting a sufficient period of time, it was learned that another organization had received a contract to do the required research and development work. The recipient of the contract, in response to the second purchase request, had slightly underbid the organization which generated the new conditions. The above may seem unfair; however, a good research and development group must not only be able to generate good ideas, it must also be able to carry them through in a competitive manner.

If the support of the research effort is from internal or company funds, it is important that top management have a tolerant attitude towards research. This attitude should not be one of charity if the company is to prosper. As has been illustrated time and time again in popular articles, many companies have current product lines which were not even conceptual ideas ten years ago. Therefore, the process of staying in business in a modern technological era requires a good research effort.

The company-funded R and D organization may initially be established by an allocation of men, money, and facilities together with a charter that sets forth certain prescribed goals. This charter will be of a general nature and may not describe in exact detail what is to be done. However, the usual aim of any organization doing research is to generate knowledge which can be utilized commercially for profit. In the case of a commercial firm, *profit* eventually takes the form of money. In the case of a nonprofit organization *profit* may be opportunity for students to support themselves while going to school, enhancement of reputation, availability of equipment, etc.

The economic or dollar payoff of basic research is usually more remote than that of development. Consequently, any organization which is under pressure to show economic worth has a strong tendency to favor development. If this is done, then existing ideas and products will be elaborated upon through the application of developmental techniques to produce new products and processes which have good immediate sales prospects. This situation does not, in the long run, bring a company to a position of leadership in its field.

One way by which economic factors can be prevented from becoming the major driving force in the R and D organization is the stabilization of the R and D budget. This can be accomplished by allocating to the research organization a fixed portion of the gross sales of the company. To illustrate the reason for this type of support, it is interesting to consider the experience of a new-products division, the research and development organization, of a large corporation. For some time, this company had the practice of allowing its various production divisions to contract with the new-products division, for work directed towards furnishing new products and, accordingly, more profit for the sponsoring divisions. Hence, many production divisions of the company utilized the new-products division as a profit making adjunct to their operations. As soon as economic difficulties were encountered in a production division, the first budgetary slash occurred in the programs being conducted by the new-products division. And, as is often the case, when one division was in trouble several others were feeling the necessity of trimming costs. Therefore, any small economic recession found the new-products division devoid of support. In times of prosperity the division had too much work and could not satisfy all of the production divisions. This situation did little to encourage the acceptance of the new-products division as anything but a subcontractor. At the same time, because of the wide fluctuations of support, the operation of a satisfactory R and D effort was impossible. The above condition was relieved when the R and D effort was funded from a fixed percentage of gross sales. Although this type of operation is influenced by the general prosperity of the company, it is much better than that previously used since the budget of the new-products division is more stable and not dependent on the largess of the other divisions. If it is economically possible, the company should support the R and D effort from a certain percentage of the gross sales plus an allotment from the corporate surplus. With this type of support the new-products division of the foregoing company could become a true research group and not just operate as a profit expander for the other divisions.

The above example illustrates the process by which an organization, set up initially to help production divisions make profits, can become a true research and development operation. All research and development should not stop in the production divisions. It should be evident, however, that a central operation is established which will have the capability of doing good research and which will give the company an opportunity to become a leader in its field.

Selecting Potential Research Programs

Because research and development divisions usually have limited budgets, which are often unstable, judicious evaluation and careful selection of R and D projects are of vital importance. From a practical viewpoint, this aspect of research and development planning and administration is most critical. In many cases an appreciable number of programs, which do not conflict with the purpose of the main corporation, are available. In fact, since the advent of diversification, the interests of large companies have become so varied that it is difficult to find areas in which they have little interest or no curiosity. For instance, automobile manufacturers make refrigerators, television sets, various home appliances, farm machinery, and a host of other items too numerous to mention. Of course, this is not true of smaller companies where product lines may involve items in only one or, at most, a few fields. However, once the interest of the company is established, then the financial support available takes over and, to a large extent, determines the scope of the research effort. Despite the desires of the researchers, management can allocate only a few percent of the net sales to the research effort.

Figure 1–10 shows company-financed research and development as a percentage of net sales for 1961. It can be seen that the percentage varies from industry to industry; however, as previously indicated, it does not vary appreciably from year to year. This figure also indicates how the industries, by securing outside support, predominantly government, increase their R and D efforts.

In many cases, certain research programs will have priority due to their obvious effect on the company's continued existence and growth. An example of this type of research need is the case where a company is dependent upon a high-grade raw material and anticipates the exhaustion of its supply of this basic ingredient. The necessity of finding a substitute material or a substitute process for utilizing low-grade material economically is evident. The exhaustion of the high-grade iron ore in the Mesabi range has spurred the hunt for conversion processes using low-grade ores. It has also encouraged the search for new iron-ore fields such as those being developed in Canada, Venezuela, Africa, etc. This research and exploration effort is an example of the sagaciousness on the part of top management's research director, which is extremely necessary for survival in a competitive market. Such foresightedness results from a research-oriented effort, which, in other words, is an organized attempt by the company to assure its continuation and welfare.

In some large companies the decision to perform research in selected areas is based upon a *make-or-buy* analysis. In our complex industrial society, large companies purchase from other companies many of the components required in their basic products. Many large corporations, which in the past purchased much of the material that went into their final product, now process or manufacture these items for themselves. For instance, it is not uncommon for automobile companies to manufacture their own electrical components, engines, bodies, paints, plastics, and accessories. In fact, many corporations are so diversified in their overall operation that they have capabilities to supply almost all of their requirements. This includes even basic raw materials, material transportation systems, etc. In some cases they even supply the public financing for the purchase of the items they sell. The financing or selling-on-time business is now so profitable that it is often possible to make more profit by dealing in credit than on the manufacturing and selling of products. The only difficulty in this chain of events is that a product is necessary before it can be sold on credit. The decision to become independent of external supply sources is usually a result of extensive operational analyses. If a decision is made to produce rather than buy an item, then a research and development effort will be necessary in order to establish and reorient the capabilities of the company in the new field. The dangers of growing too self-sufficient are obvious. Antitrust laws and other legal complications may have a major effect on any decision to expand a large operation to a self-sufficient or monopolistic position.

When a research program with its attendant priorities has been established, the research manager is faced with the problem of allocating his research budget in a manner which will offer the best possibility of obtaining the objectives set forth in the program. This distribution of funds into project areas is a difficult task. Two of the most important factors which influence the utilization of the research funds are: the cost of the research effort; and the contribution that the research effort will provide to the growth of the parent organization in its various areas of interest. The success of the research program will to a large extent be determined by the analysis the research manager makes in regard to the two items listed above.

Methods for the analysis and evaluation of competitive research and development ventures appear continually in articles in the technical literature. These venture analysis techniques employ various analytical models to represent the relative attractiveness of the programs under consideration. Although many of these methods exist, a few seem to have gained particular popularity and are in widespread use. A brief description of the most popular techniques seems worthwhile at this point to illustrate the philosophies and complexities involved in venture analysis.

The *venture-worth* method of project analysis has been described by Happel. (See references.) This method was originally developed for comparing the attractiveness of various technically proven projects. The extension of the *venture-worth* method to R and D undertakings involves greater complexities because of the fact that the probability of success must enter into the analysis. Many economic factors also affect the decision to proceed or not proceed into a development program. For example, the desirability or necessity for getting to production ahead of competition may outweigh certain other economic facets that may be unattractive.

Another method of venture analysis proposes the evaluation of project attractiveness on the basis of a weight-factored consideration of research cost, research incentive, and penalty for delay. The analysis is begun with the determination of the estimated research costs and incentives. The research costs include, in addition to the more obvious expenses, exploratory, marketing research and development, and economic analysis costs. A reliable estimate of research costs will usually result if data on the expenditures associated with similar research and development projects of the past are available. The estimate of research incentives is an attempt to affix a dollar value to such factors as reduction of operating costs, improvement in production rate, creation of new and profitable products, process integration, automation potential, rate at which application can be achieved, potentiality for licensing, etc. All of these items can be weight-factored in accordance with the particular objectives or aspirations of the company or organization. The last item of this evaluation is an assessment of penalties for delay in initiating a project. Although this is the most difficult part of the evaluation, money values can usually be assigned to these penalties after careful study. Hence, this technique of venture analysis actually replaces one large decision by a number of much smaller decisions. When the three factors have been determined and combined, they represent an index of attractiveness for immediate investment in the venture. Thus, with a determination of this type available for each of several competitive projects, the most attractive ones can be selected for funding with the available budget.

Simplified evaluation methods based upon the determination of several qualitative indices have been proposed. Although the forms of the indices proposed are usually tailored for ventures associated with a particular industry, a more general form can be devised. Such a general version of the indices is provided in Table 4–1 and should prove to be useful. The basis for evaluation

TABLE 4–1

QUALITATIVE RATING SYSTEM FOR R AND D PROJECTS

A. *Payoff Period, in Percent of Maximum Permissible Period t_m*	B. *Estimated Cash Position after Ten Years, in Percent of Most Optimistic Value V_{10}*

Percent t_m	Points	Percent V_{10}	Points
80 –100	2	1– 20	2
65 – 79	5	20– 40	4
41 – 64	8	40– 60	6
21 – 40	11	60– 80	8
1.1– 20	14	80–100	10 (max)
0.6– 1.0	17		
0– 0.5	20 (max)		

C. *Chances of Success*	D. *Other Pertinent Factors*

Chances	Points
poor	2
uncertain	4
fair	6
good	8
excellent	10 (max)

1. Advantageous Competitive Raw Materials Position: yes(1); no (0).
2. Established Sales Outlet or Internal Use: yes (1); no (0).
3. Compatible with Present Product Line or Objectives: yes (1); no (0).
4. Low or Reasonable Plant Investment: yes (1); no (0).
5. Potentiality for Royalties, Patents, etc.: yes (1); no (0).
6. Availability of R&D Manpower: yes (1); no (0).
7. Early Market Penetration: yes (1); no (0).
8. Long Life Expectancy for the Product Market: yes (1); no (0).
9. Moderate or Reasonable R&D Expenditure: yes (1); no (0).
10. Uniqueness of Product Properties Sufficient to Create a Distinct Market Advantage: yes (1); no (0).

(Maximum possible total of 10 points.)

of each project has a maximum of fifty points. Those projects which score the highest are to be regarded as most attractive.

The techniques for venture analysis discussed are not

the only ones that have been proposed. Many more suggested methods can be found in the literature. None, however, can be regarded as a substitute for well-founded and considered judgment on the part of research managers. In fact, all of the techniques available are merely situation simulators which can provide a basis for decisions but which, in themselves, cannot provide the administrator with his decision neatly wrapped in a package.

Orienting Development Programs

Although the development manager may not initially set the overall funding for his program effort, his counsel and advice may be sought by higher management. As a result, he may have an appreciable influence on the program's funding. In addition, the allocation of overall funds to various program elements is extremely important, and will determine the extent to which the results of the effort are optimized.

Figure 4–1 illustrates how poor planning can delay a project completion date. When the incentive or charter has been given to the development manager, he and his staff must make a complete analysis of the requirements for the project or, as indicated on the figure, the end system. This system may require two or more subsystems which, upon integration, will make up the final product. These systems must each be engineered, developed, and, in many cases, supported by applied research. In some cases basic or breakthrough research must be conducted. As indicated in the figure, the end objective will not be satisfied until all of the subsystems are completed. As shown, subsystems B and C will be finished prior to the completion of the total system. The successful completion of a subsystem before other subsystems are ready indicates possible inadequacies in overall planning. Proper allocation of funds among the various project components usually makes it possible to shorten the time required for project completion. Although an earlier date of completion for a subsystem may seem to suggest

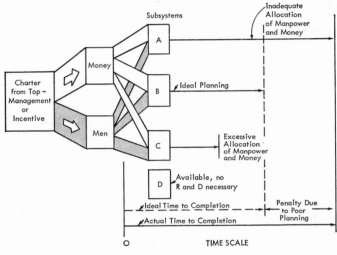

FIG. 4–1

Money and Time Relationships Associated with
Development Projects

efficient utilization of manpower and money, in reality it stems either from poor overall planning or from a break-through which simplified the problem. The purpose of the foregoing is to indicate that the development manager must always plan, replan, orient, and reorient his overall program. By proper application of money and time an optimum program may be approached. Program planning will be discussed in more detail in Chapter 7.

Because successful research and development effort is not as easy to plan as is production, and because it is influenced by factors not always amenable to logical reasoning, it will be commonplace for subsystems to be completed prior to or after planned dates. If project resources can readily be shifted from one subproject to others, then the main project may not be unduly delayed. However, in many cases, the manpower required on one system cannot be utilized on another. This then is where inefficient preliminary planning handicaps the overall program.

Usually a many-systemed research and development program is predicated on the extrapolation of existing knowledge. Suppose, for instance, that a new airplane is to be built. The general engine requirements are known; however, the engine is still a design on paper. Let the engine subsystem be called system A. The airframe has been designed; however, it will use new exotic materials. The airframe is subsystem B. The control system must perform with response times faster than those previously required. This is subsystem C. As is very evident, the failure of any subsystem will imperil the overall project. Fortunately, in the extrapolations suggested above, a good background of knowledge exists and the possibility of failure is somewhat reduced. Nevertheless, even now it is not uncommon for new aircraft to encounter difficulty in meeting specifications and requirements. Many other types of programs, also, have failed because certain complex technical problems could not be solved within reasonable time periods.

Despite the difficulty of planning projects for which major breakthroughs are required, it is vitally necessary that control over project resources be maintained. It is also important for an industrial organization to limit corporate spending on large projects that rely greatly upon many breakthroughs. In this realm it is sometimes desirable to secure government support. By this means, the company may make some profit even if the project is unsuccessful. This does not mean that corporations should shun breakthrough research work completely. They should undertake it on a scale in keeping with their overall sizes and capabilities. The following rules are important:

1. Large breakthrough projects should be performed, where possible, on cost reimbursement contracts for the government.
2. Close financial and manpower control should be maintained on large, research-development projects.
3. The best manpower available should be used on research and development programs, particularly on high-risk, breakthrough, types of projects.

Summary

Industrial research and development should be oriented in a direction which amplifies and extends the capabilities of the sponsoring company. This requires that top management understand the objectives and the status of their current research programs. Further, persons in upper-echelon management positions should comprehend the necessity for and attractiveness of new projects proposed for future support. This understanding, when combined with the primary purpose of the corporation, will enable managers to make decisions in regard to the allocation of men and money for various research programs.

Men, materials, and time are required for the accomplishment of desired objectives. Research managers are saddled with the responsibility of scheduling, distributing, and optimizing these three ingredients in their research operations to achieve profitable results. The relative quantities of each ingredient that are needed, versus those available, impose important restrictions upon the direction and extent of research and development orientation.

Funds for research and development will probably be derived from company profits if the objective of the programs is the improvement, amplification, or extension of the company's product line in the commercial market. If the organization desires to expand its research program it may be beneficial to attempt to supplement company funds with support from government contracts. It is important that company research and development organizations be funded on a continuing basis with a fairly stable fiscal budget.

Nonprofit research organizations and universities are usually funded from gifts, endowments, government contracts, industrial contracts, and grants.

The most important and difficult phase of research orientation is the evaluation of potential programs and the selection of those which are most lucrative. Because research and development budgets are usually modest, careful evaluation methods must be applied to screen out only a few high-potential programs for support. The fraction of the total available budget to be allocated to the various selected programs must be proportional to the relative attractiveness or potential of each. Several methods for project evaluation have been proposed in the literature. These range from complex analytical models requiring detailed parametric input, to simplified qualitative techniques which reduce the analysis from one involving a single, complex decision, to several, less-complicated decisions based upon attractiveness factors. For most industrial situations the qualitative techniques are probably adequate.

The orientation of development effort differs from

that for research because a development operation is usually larger in requirements for men and materials and involves fewer high risk elements. Therefore, the orientation process becomes one of allocating and scheduling available resources among segments of the program to accomplish one large objective. In complex projects which rely upon technological breakthroughs for their successful completion, the risks are greater and closer control of manpower and money is required. In addition, programs of this type demand the best project personnel available. The high risk to the organization often can be reduced through government contracts to partially support the effort.

Chapter 5

The Origin of Research Ideas

VIRTUALLY anything the mind of man can conceive he can accomplish. This statement in a few words points out one of the most important aspects of research and development—*the creation of new concepts and ideas.* Before anything can be accomplished an idea must be planted in fertile ground where it can germinate and blossom forth. The important step in this process is not the planting of the idea, or even the husbanding of it to fruition, but rather its acquisition. Therefore, it is important for researchers to understand the genesis of ideas and the conditions which encourage their rapid production. For research organizations, the generation of creative and useful ideas is of the utmost importance because these organizations sell ideas and not hardware-type products. In contrast with automobile salesmen who can become well acquainted with their product, research salesmen, in many cases, do not have a completely clear idea of what they are selling. This is partially due to the fact that if the end result of the research could have been predicted then the work itself may not have been necessary.

It is the purpose of this chapter to point out factors involved in the generation of ideas. These may be used by individuals to stimulate latent creative talents.

Concepts of Creativity

From the origin of mankind, creativity has been associated with a small number of people in each age. In the stone age such individuals introduced the use of fire, invented weapons, created tools, and initiated the conversion of natural phenomena for the comfort and betterment of man.

For centuries the small population of the world, the lack of communication between various groups, and the lack of mass education made the progress associated with new ideas slow. Today, with the advances in communication and education which allow the dissemination and incorporation of past creative ideas into our civilization base, the generation of new ideas has correspondingly increased. Innovators and other creative individuals are currently working in virtually every field of human endeavor. Also, the world is receptive to new ideas, resulting in an almost exponential growth in industrial progress and capabilities.

If a given number of people are studied it will be found that only a small fraction are truly creative, a larger number may or may not be creative depending on their opportunities and environment, and the majority will rarely have an original thought. Consequently, the staff of a research organization should be selected from the first two groups mentioned above. The first group will undoubtedly originate much of the basic research, and the second will be useful in the applied and developmental aspects of research. The last and largest group is useful for producing the products which the researcher develops.

How do people obtain ideas? This question has long

plagued persons who are interested in making their livings from inventions or who are interested in discovering new products or even creating new aspects of old products. It is not uncommon to hear it said about an individual: *"He never had an idea in his whole life."* It is also common to hear some people tagged with the comment: *"He's full of ideas."* What is the difference between these two types of individuals? It is not necessarily intelligence or industriousness which were discussed before; it appears to be a difference in attitude toward the world at large.

The creative individual is distinguished by his speculative nature. He cannot let well enough alone; he always wants to change things; he continually strives to create new concepts; and he always wants to modify equipment, processes, and methods, for their improvement. The noncreative individual, on the other hand, is usually unimaginative and conservative, and frequently resists change. He is the type of individual who is content with the world as it is. He does not wish to see change which might upset his mode of living. Are people born with creative ability or is it possible to develop this talent? It appears that creativity is partially inherited and partially influenced by environment.

If an individual is endowed with the ability to create ideas and new things, this ability can be improved and channeled into a more productive capability by proper training. It is somewhat similar to musical talent which, with proper training, reaches a peak of perfection. If a potential musician does not receive proper training and encouragement and if he is not exposed to the wealth of musical knowledge which is available in the world, it is quite possible that his talent will fall on barren ground and not blossom forth. Without education, without opportunity, and without the proper environment, the creative individual is less likely to become the successful inventor, scientist, creative artist, etc. If the principles of creativity can be determined, then like any other educational procedure, they may be applied to promote efficient use of researchers' creative mental machinery. With proper application of this knowledge, utilization of the creative individual can be improved.

It is not sufficient just to wish to be creative. Creativity, like any other intellectual process, usually calls for continuing and intense mental effort. Einstein could have wished for years to be creative without results. Instead, he utilized and exercised his talent.

In general, the inductive mental process has five characteristics. These can be grouped into five categories:

1. *Collection of Facts*
   This is the process by which the individual studies the factors and circumstances pertaining to the problem which he wishes to tackle. He completes an exhaustive search for all the known facts about the subject. He talks to people who are working in the field. In general, he attempts to uncover all known and pertinent information which is available.

2. *Review and Preliminary Analysis*
   Through this process the researcher assimilates the information which he has been collecting. He looks at all aspects of the problem. He approaches it from different angles, and, in general, he considers what he could accomplish by utilizing all the observed data in various combinations and forms.

3. *Application of Experience*
   In this step, the researcher recalls pertinent information from his memory and applies this information to his current problem. Remembering is one of the important facets of creative thinking, and is perhaps the most important process which is utilized by good research

and development managers. Here it takes the form of intuition. To a large extent, if you ask a very good research manager why he does certain things, he may not be able to give you specific analytical reasons; however, based upon his past experience, he just knows what to do in a given situation.

4. *Analysis*

   By analysis the researcher determines the effect that changes in or combinations of the pertinent things he collected, reviewed, and remembered will have on the final purpose of his work. Analyzing, therefore, is the logical assembly and interpretation of the information which has been accumulated.

5. *Development of Conclusions*

   This is the process by which the researcher arrives at a deduction from the hard work of collecting information, and the strain of remembering and analyzing pertinent factors. The process of concluding is a very important aspect of a research effort, especially from an economic standpoint.

The above five characteristics are purely noncreative in themselves and can easily be applied by any intelligent individual. If they are utilized fully, it will be possible to reach conclusions which, in some cases, may appear to be creative. Actually, the characteristics discussed are merely the basis of logical thinking. Logical thinking is one of the tools which the creative individual must employ. This tool, however, is not sufficient in itself to accomplish the generation of new ideas. Another aspect of creativity is vital, and involves the following two processes:

1. *Imagination*

   The ability to form mental images of objects which are not presented to the senses is imagination. It is a mental synthesis of various ideas into a new concept. It is the power of inventing the novel by recombining the elements of reality. Combined with inspiration, imagination can create new ideas from combinations of old ideas and observed information.

2. *Enlightenment*

Enlightenment is inspiration which comes as a result of the work which has gone on before. It is not the result of conscious effort. An idea may strike a person suddenly while on the golf course, in the shower, or driving to work. Enlightenment seems to come from deep down within the individual. It does not appear to be a characteristic which can be trained or called upon at will. Some individuals have it, some do not. However, it will not show itself if the proper preparation has not been taken in establishing the base for the solution of the problem or the need for the desired idea. In other words, the work of collecting and reviewing facts, remembering, analyzing, etc., must have preceded the enlightenment stage.

Motivating and Encouraging Creativity

While it is possible for an individual to have a high potential for creative activity, it is still possible for him to be very ineffective in creating new ideas. This may result from the environment in which he works. If the environment requires that the individual conform to unwise policies, if the environment requires him to accomplish uninteresting tasks, and if the environment does not allow him the free run of his imagination, then, in all probability, creativity will be stifled. It is not uncommon for a very imaginative young researcher, who is placed under a domineering older scientist, to lose some of his creativity because he is not allowed the opportunity of making his own mistakes. Overcontrol by supervisors will undoubtedly suppress the creative bent of many individuals. If possible, creative individuals should be allowed a portion of their time to utilize as they see fit.

However, they should be encouraged to utilize their time in fruitful pursuits for the organization and not just as a means of self-aggrandizement. An organization is handicapped appreciably if employees are too much concerned with their own affairs.

One director of a large research organization tells his administrators that they should not give too many tasks to the young scientist. The reasoning behind this is his conviction that many young men have been ruined, so to speak, by being overloaded. The creative process is not something which can be rapidly applied to a problem and assure a solution. It is a process which indicates, after a period of time, a method by which a solution, if one is available, may be obtained. It may not work if it is applied too hurriedly.

Research and development administrators soon realize that the management of creative personnel is very difficult and complex. In general, management serves, or should serve, creative individuals by stimulating, assisting with routine details, and encouraging creative activity wherever it is recognized. It should also, since our civilization is one which is based upon economic values, assure that the creative individual is rewarded for his efforts. If he is encouraged, stimulated, and rewarded, then the creative man will operate at a relatively high efficiency for the benefit of the whole organization.

The research manager has an extremely difficult problem in determining the level of stimulation, encouragement, and assistance required by the individuals on his staff. The stimulation required by one individual may be too great for another. The encouragement required by one individual may be too great for another. Therefore, the research manager should make sure that he utilizes the tools of stimulation, encouragement, assistance, and reward judiciously in an effort neither to overplay nor, conversely, underplay their importance in his development of creative manpower.

Creative individuals differ in their ability to work towards deadlines. Some can meet stringent time requirements, whereas others are frustrated and confused if they are held to a strict timetable. Of course, before a person can be allowed unlimited time, which in the final analysis is money, it is important that he be of proven worth. This brings up the question of how to determine the creative individual. One method of evaluation is the rate of production and quality of his scientific results and reports. Another is his inventions or discoveries which have economic benefit to the organization.

Many tests are available to determine extent of interest, intelligence, personality problems, and the like; however, a specific test for creativity has as yet not been developed which will satisfactorily rate this most elusive characteristic. Past performance is, therefore, the most important factor by which to rate a researcher. As stated in one of the earlier chapters, the creative individual probably will have in his childhood innovated and created toys, new games, or other interesting and unique items. Perhaps he will have made a new type of model airplane. Perhaps he will have made a new type of scooter. Perhaps he will have built a new type of computer or even toy gun. Be this as it may, the creative individual will usually show his talent at an early age. Throughout life, in college, in his first job, etc., the creative researcher will have come up with unique ideas, from time to time, which are representative of his creative ability. *Therefore, to determine the creative individual examine his past performance.*

If creative individuals are discovered and placed in an

environment which is conducive to creativity, namely an environment in which ideas can grow, then creative effort will be generated. If the environment requires many administrative tasks, excessive committee work, etc., the creativity will be stifled.

With respect to the management of creative endeavor, the most important tasks of research and development administrators are:

1. The discovery of creative individuals;
2. The maintenance of an environment conducive to creative activity; and,
3. The utilization of the results of creativity for the benefit of their organizations.

Channeling of Creative Ideas

If the staff of an organization generates creative ideas, it is important that the organization protect these assets by proper legal means. One important legal document which protects the organization from unethical practices by its staff is the employee patent agreement. Personnel hired to work on research and development projects should all be required to sign an agreement which delineates their rights and their responsibilities to the parent organization. After an invention has been discovered, the primary method of protection is by obtaining a patent.

It should be apparent that patents, etc., are assets just as are hard items like buildings, machinery, etc. It is important that the inventor, the creator of these assets, be rewarded financially with some tangible token of appreciation. If the organization has a patent-sharing policy, usually delineated in the employee patent agreement, then this will be accomplished. Reward programs make the inventor feel that he is deriving a benefit for himself as well as for the company through his creative effort. This benefit to the inventor need not be large: what is important is that the organization recognizes the value of the researcher's efforts.

The rewarding of employees both financially and in status for creative effort will do much to establish a proper environment for the continuation of productive endeavor. Ideas generated by researchers must be recognized, rewarded, and utilized if they are to be of value. Hence, by proper handling and channeling of ideas from conception to application, the environment for economic creativity will be maintained.

Group Approach to Idea Generation

During the past several years the process of *brain storming* has been used for the generation of new ideas and concepts. In this process, a group of individuals from various disciplines gets together to analyze a problem. They submit comments or ideas with hopes for a rapid solution to the problem by inspirational means. This process is supposed to create new ideas which are not inhibited by the normal restraints of the working environment and the contemporaries of the individuals concerned. Ideas are proposed for consideration and utilized if applicable. The system of *brain storming* has many advocates. Perhaps it has some utility. However, it may be that the time spent collectively by the various researchers in *brain storming* would be more fruitful if utilized individually in a creative manner. By proper collection of facts, review and analysis, and using the inspirational method, individuals can obtain results which will probably be superior to those obtained by the group approach.

If a *brain storming* group has sufficient preparation and education before the group meets, perhaps it too can come up with sufficient ideas to justify its existence. However, *brain storming* activities appear to be committee efforts which are expensive in time and manpower and, consequently, should be avoided unless the environment for creativity in the organization is such that only a *brain storming* session, with specific instructions to think widely and without restraint, will facilitate freedom of thought and expression.

In large organizations individual freedom of action and expression are often suppressed, and an outgrowth of this situation is the use of committees for concerted group action. It appears that *brain storming* is an extension of the committee approach to research endeavor. In many cases, it is necessary to utilize committees to obtain information for the use of the administrator and his staff in making decisions, and for this purpose committees are valuable. For instance, it may be important to determine whether or not a certain research operation should be undertaken. In this case, the administrator alone may not have sufficient technical information on which to base a decision and must, therefore, rely on his technical staff discussions to point the way for him. If, however, an administrator does not wish to make a decision on some problem, then the committee may become his way of passing on or diffusing his responsibility.

It appears that the group approach to the generation of creative ideas has less chance of fruitful results than the individual approach. If the group consists of many creative individuals the group environment is not conducive for optimum creative output. If the group consists of noncreative individuals then it will probably not be prolific in the production of good ideas. An as yet unanswered question is, *"What critical mass of noncreative individuals equals one creative thinker?"*

Summary

In this chapter the concepts of creativity were discussed. The basic processes which are fundamental to the creative mental process were described. They are collection of facts, review, application of experience, analysis, and development of conclusions. The five processes themselves are noncreative, but they are the base on which creativity rests. The collection of facts places the available information in proper perspective to the current problem. Review is the consideration of the information from various directions and in different ways. Application of experience involves the recall from memory of items that relate to the problem. The process of analysis utilizes the reasoning powers of the individual. Finally, the concluding process provides a deduction from the effort associated with the other four processes. Without these five necessary ingredients no significant progress can be made towards the solution of any problem.

In addition to the above five noncreative processes are the creative processes of imagination and enlightenment. Imagination is the utilization and recombination of old ideas into new concepts. Enlightenment is an intangible characteristic of creative individuals whereby they suddenly, almost inspirationally, obtain answers to problems at moments when they least expect them. This characteristic of creative individuals is generally not present in noncreative persons, and seems to be the essential ingredient for creativity.

Many methods of motivating and encouraging creativity exist. One method is to provide a good environment—one which gives some freedom to the researcher. He should be permitted to think freely and encouraged to explore both ideas which he believes will benefit the overall operation of the organization and new areas of research effort where the economic benefits are not obvious. It is realized that any organization has economic limitations which prevent it from allowing unlimited freedom to its researchers. Another method of motivating research is to encourage and reward new ideas or successful solutions to problems. This includes patent profit sharing programs, incentive rewards, etc.

Good supervisors should see that creative researchers are not unduly hampered with mundane and routine tasks. They should be permitted to utilize their talents in the most efficient and expeditious manner. They should not be burdened with tasks which any clerk can do.

The group approach to idea generation has been used in the past. It may provide some benefits to certain types of operations. However, the best method of solving problems appears to be the use of the five basic steps—collection of facts, review, application of experience, analysis, and development of conclusions—by creative individuals. All too often, committee and group efforts are utilized by weak administrators who are unwilling to assume responsibility for their decisions.

The most important ingredient in the creative endeavor is the creative individual.

Chapter 6

Proposal Preparation
and Sales Effort

BEFORE A research project can be initiated, an idea is necessary on which to base the program and the request for funding. This idea must be relatively clear in the mind of the research manager or researcher. Although it need not anticipate the answer to the research problem, it should outline what steps will be taken to obtain the possible answers. After the decision to conduct research is made and before large sums of money are allocated, effective top managers will require the research staff to outline in detail the procedures and aims of the proposed research effort. In general, any research program for sponsorship by corporate, government, or industrial funds must be presented in a written form to some decision-making body which determines whether or not it should be supported. This written presentation is called a *proposal*.

In large research organizations, which depend upon outside sponsorship for their operation, the *proposal* is a principal factor in their existence. It describes the product that is sold to the sponsor. In the case of research, the product for sale is an idea or a group of ideas which presents a program for the economic or strategic benefit of the sponsor. The manner in which the proposal is written, the relationship between the proposed effort and dollar value, and the methods by which the proposal is presented for sale to potential sponsors are all important factors which must be carefully considered by the researcher, the research manager, and the contracting staff.

As is obvious, research programs cannot be guaranteed to produce satisfaction. In some cases applied or development research may be conducted on fixed price agreements; however, it is usually unwise for a research organization to guarantee results since research, by its very nature, is an exploration of the unknown. If precise information is available on which to establish a fixed price for the work then in reality the project is not research. Rather, it is routine testing with perhaps a small amount of development effort included.

The writing of proposals for potential sponsors should not be taken casually or regarded as unimportant. If unintelligible and carelessly written proposals are submitted they are of little value. A proposal should be grammatically correct, easy to read, and contain the description of a logical research program. *The proposal is immensely important to the research organization.*

A skillfully prepared proposal will have the following five features:

1. It will completely describe the program and the ideas on which the program of research is based.
2. It will not contain extraneous material but will be concise and to the point.
3. It will be clear in meaning and easily understood. It will not contain words which are infrequently used. It will not have format which, although correct, is not clear in context. It will be easy to read.
4. It will be as technically correct as possible.

5. Its tone will be appropriate so that false impressions will not be imparted to the reader or potential sponsor.

With respect to the first item above, a question the writer should ask himself is, *"Does this proposal give all the information necessary to indicate to the reader the purpose of the proposed research program?"* Another question he should ask is, *"Does this proposal anticipate answers to questions which an intelligent reader would logically be expected to ask?"* It is obvious that if the proposal answers these questions and if it has technical value it is much more likely to be well received.

Clarity is one of the most difficult qualities to obtain in the proposal. Almost everyone who works in a large organization has experienced the *instructional memorandum* which is so vague and improperly written that it only causes confusion. This confusion is more expensive, in many cases, than the original problem which the memorandum attempted to solve. If potential sponsors are continually requesting additional information on proposals which have been submitted to them, this probably indicates inadequate proposal preparation procedures in regard to clearness and completeness. It also points out the need for an examination of the organization's proposal preparation system.

In some cases, incompleteness can be justified. A proposal which describes a problem for which a solution approach is being sought may of necessity be a little vague. Nevertheless, the proposal should explain the reasons for the vagueness and, at the same time, bring to the attention of the reader the state-of-the-art concerning the problem posed. This will give the reader an insight into the reasons for the research, the possible advantages which might accrue from the research, and will eliminate questions concerning incompleteness of the proposal.

In the foregoing paragraphs the term "completeness" was emphasized. Completeness, however, should not be achieved at the expense of conciseness. It is possible to take a small idea, write a book on it, and then submit this book as a proposal. This, of course, is carrying the idea of completeness to an extreme. Completeness can coexist with conciseness if the proposal is prepared with care. In order to determine conciseness, another important question the writer of the proposal should ask is, *"Does this proposal contain only the essential facts?"* Many writers tend to put in extraneous data, including volumes of miscellaneous unrelated facts. This unnecessary information tends to confuse the reader. The proposal should include only the essential information and descriptions necessary to describe the proposed work adequately.

People who evaluate proposals and commit large sums of money for research effort are usually very busy individuals. They do not have the patience to be burdened with unnecessary details. However, they are usually thorough and intelligent enough to require that pertinent information, on which they can make logical decisions, is available before they make these decisions. Therefore, the researcher who is writing a proposal must make his proposal serve this purpose. An effort to balance completeness and conciseness will not only help the writer present his ideas in a logical and thoughtful manner, it will also make a good impression upon the potential sponsor of the work.

In addition to being complete and concise, a proposal should also be clear in meaning and comprehensible to people of various disciplines. In all probability, a proposal will be read by several individuals before it is either rejected or supported. Consequently, the funding of the proposal may depend upon whether or not the information presented has the same meaning to every person who has read it. It may seem that if a proposal were complete and concise it would also be clear in meaning; however, this is not true and it is the function of the question, *"Is it clear?"*, to emphasize that completeness and conciseness do not necessarily assure that the information is presented in a form which can be easily and quickly understood. A physician can write a brief paragraph in technical language directed to his profession which would indicate the prognosis of an operation or a disease. This sentence or paragraph would be clear to other physicians; however, it would not be clear to the ordinary nonmedical and nontechnical layman or even to the scientist or engineer.

In regard to clarity, it is necessary that the language and jargon used in the proposal be adapted to the potential readers. The words that are used should be the simplest which will convey the ideas being presented. Even the best educated and the most intelligent readers are irritated by long streams of words which, although correct, produce sentences that are hard to interpret. This can happen even when the meanings of all the words are clear. Hence, the proposal writer needs to make certain that his words and sentences convey his ideas in the simplest and easiest to read manner possible.

The fourth of the initial five items considered for effective writing poses the question, *"Is the information correct?"* Nothing can damage a proposal more than to have it contain information which is obviously incorrect. Engineering and science are advancing so rapidly that concepts, which were thought to be true several years ago are no longer considered to be up-to-date and valid. Therefore, a researcher who is selling his ideas in a research proposal should ascertain the accuracy and time-liness of the ideas. This may be partially accomplished by an exhaustive literature survey on the subject under consideration. However, the information explosion of the past few years makes access to all the pertinent information practically impossible. For example, foreign journals may not be readily available to the researcher. Sometimes this difficulty can be ameliorated by the researcher through personal contacts with the potential sponsor. In these personal contacts, the researcher can discuss the current state-of-the-art of the program and, thereby, obtain information from the proposed sponsor as to what is considered important.

In any written presentation, correct grammar, punc-tuation, and spelling are primary in the effect they have on the reader's overall impression. Errors in usage of words, sentence construction, spelling, etc., greatly de-tract from a technical proposal. The reader is inclined to regard these errors as an index to the general attitude and ability of the writer and his organization and to forecast similar abandon on their part should the pro-posal receive support.

The final ingredient required in a good proposal is a proper tone. Tone refers not to what was said in the proposal but how it was said. As a result, it is a difficult quality to evaluate. In order to sell a research program, the proposal must be read and acted upon. If the reading of the proposal is difficult and dreary, then it is difficult to get the proposal read. If the reading of the proposal is interesting, if illustrations are included which make the project come to life, then the tone of the proposal is excellent and the reader will feel a friendliness toward the submitting organization and the writer. If the tone is improper, if the proposal is written in an antagonistic manner, then the reader will probably be alienated to the detriment of the chances of support for the research work. Tone, therefore, is extremely important in a good research proposal. The writer of a proposal should not be arbitrary in his propositions; he should not be indifferent to the interests of others; he should not be grudging in his credit to others; he should not be flatly and dogmatically contradictory of other researchers in his references; he should not be insulting in his remarks; and he should not be insolent or tactless in any statement. With respect to the work which he proposes to do, he should not be apologetic or weak in presenting what he hopes to accomplish; however, he should not promise results which cannot be justified on the basis of the known facts. The writer should not write down to the level of the reader. Instead, he should write for the reader's technical level. In general, it can be said that the tone of the proposal is an important factor in determining whether or not the research program is accepted for support.

In the foregoing, five items which should be considered in preparing a proposal were discussed. Consideration of these items indicated that writing a proposal is not an easy task and should not be taken lightly. It is something that should be worked at diligently and conscientiously.

Government Sponsored Research

If an organization desires to seek federal funds for research and development, a knowledge of the types of R and D contracts that can be obtained and the federal agencies which support these contracts is necessary. This information will provide the basis for a well-planned sales activity. In addition, a knowledge of the accepted proposal format is helpful.

The Department of Defense (Army, Navy, and Air

Force) and the National Aeronautics and Space Administration support a large portion of the research and development effort in the country. In the Department of Defense, a Director of Research and Engineering supervises the Advanced Research Projects Agency. This agency is usually referred to as ARPA, and it handles large projects which have military applications in the ballistic missile, space, and related areas. This agency has a legal right to contract directly with outside organizations; however, it negotiates practically all of its contracts through existing contracting groups of the three agencies of the Department of Defense. The following is a listing of the key offices of the various Department of Defense agencies which are interested in basic research.

1. *Advanced Research Projects Agency*

This agency is a separately organized research and development group under the Department of Defense. It is responsible for basic and applied research and development projects as assigned by the Director of Defense Research and Engineering. The agency utilizes the services of the military departments, other government agencies, private industry, individuals, and research and educational institutions to perform its projects.

2. *Air Force Office of Scientific Research*

This agency operates under the direction of the Air Force Research Division of the United States Air Force. Concerned with the operation of this agency is the Scientific Advisory Board which performs consultative services pertaining to scientific matters related to the fulfillment of the Air Force mission. The members of this board are selected from various scientific fields and make up an advisory and consultant body which reviews research and development with a viewpoint aimed towards military application. The board also reviews and evaluates the Air Force long-range plans for research and development.

3. *The Office of Naval Research*

This office is charged with the duties of planning, initiating, encouraging, and conducting naval research in augmentation of and in conjunction with the research and development activities of other agencies of the Department of the Navy. The Office of Naval Research is concerned with the worldwide findings, trends, potentialities, and achievements in research and development. It is the principal representative of the Department of the Navy in dealings of Navy-wide interest in research matters.

4. *The U.S. Army Research Office—Durham, N.C.*

This organization is assigned Army-wide responsibility for coordination and support of basic research in the physical sciences and in mathematics. It is one of many offices concerned with basic and applied research which is under the Chief, Research and Development, Department of the Army, Washington, D.C.

In the National Aeronautics and Space Administration there are several centers which conduct and which also can support basic and applied contract research. In the next decade the R and D activities of NASA will far exceed any effort expended in the past. With the space race to put a man on the moon and other aerospace programs, extremely large amounts of money will be spent on R and D efforts.

The NASA research centers may be approached with research proposals; however, for basic and applied research it is advisable to first contact the NASA Office of Research Grants and Contracts in Washington, D.C. It is the policy of NASA to encourage communication between potential researchers and its own scientists; therefore, informal proposals and discussions are welcomed. In this manner it is sometimes feasible to postpone the writing of a formal proposal until general agreement is reached on the purpose and scope of the proposed research. This does not mean to imply that NASA will define a research program for a research organization. Rather it implies that if a program is proposed, NASA will delineate wherein its interest lies.

The fact that NASA has a very extensive research capability at its many centers does not mean that it is less interested in sponsoring outside research and development activity. In fact, the enormous space program underway will strain the facilities of NASA and those of other competent research organizations if the program is to be crowned with success.

In addition to NASA and the Department of Defense, the Atomic Energy Commission, the Department of Health, Education, and Welfare, the Department of Agriculture, the National Science Foundation, the Department of Commerce, and many other government agencies are also responsible for research and development work. If a person is desirous of doing research in a particular area, he should try to contact the agency of the federal government which is interested in this type of work. It can be said with reasonable certainty that an agency can be found for almost any research area. For persons interested in doing research for the federal government, it is suggested that they obtain a copy of the United States Organization Manual from the Government Printing Office.

Preparation and Submission of Unsolicited Research Proposals

The Department of Defense, the National Aeronautics and Space Administration, the National Science Foundation, the National Institute of Health, and other government agencies are all amenable to receiving unsolicited research proposals. These proposals are submitted in accordance with various requirements which have been documented by each of the agencies. While in some cases no rigid format is specified, in others a standard format may be required or desired. If no particular format is specified, the proposals should, in general, cover the following main points:

1. The legal title and address of the organization submitting the proposal. It is important for the agency of the government to know what organization they will be contacting during the evaluation of the proposed work.

2. Title of the proposed research. The title of the proposed research should be as short and clear as possible. The title should indicate to a potential reader the field and possibly the area to which the work will pertain.

3. Time period for which support is requested. It is important to specify the estimated time duration of the proposed work because the federal agencies are interested in knowing the period of time during which funds will be required.

4. A brief abstract of the proposed research. This abstract should be short and complete and should give the cursory reader a synopsis of the proposed effort. For planning purposes, the abstract will enable the government reader to categorize the work and see that it is funneled into the right technical channel.

5. Identification of the research objectives. The research objectives should be defined as clearly as possible and the overall purpose for which the money is requested should be delineated.

6. A detailed description of the proposed method of procedure which will be used to achieve the objectives of the research effort. Here it is important that the detailed program, including documentation, which has been visualized by the researcher and writer of the proposal, be specified. This should be done in a

manner so that the reader or potential sponsor will have no difficulty in understanding the purpose for which funds are being requested, the anticipated results of the expenditures, and the possible benefits which will accrue to the sponsor as a result of the program.

7. The availability of facilities and the need for additional facilities. Proposal evaluators usually regard the facilities and capabilities of the submitting organization as an index to the economic efficiency of the proposed expenditure of funds. Requests for certain types of funding to build facilities may be regarded as inefficient utilization of federal money. In some cases the expenditure of federal funds to extend the capabilities of the organization submitting the proposal may be regarded favorably by the potential sponsor. This is particularly true in instances wherein the requirements of the proposed program are unique or when the existing facilities can be modified at a reasonable cost to provide for the proposed technical requirements. This factor becomes, therefore, an important facet in the overall program. Reasonable requests for funds to improve or establish facilities for the program should be submitted as a part of the proposal.

8. Personnel requirements. Names of key individuals and their biographical sketches containing background information should be provided. Information of this type gives the reader an indication of the competence and the technical background of personnel who will contribute to the proposed effort. A typical biographical sketch is outlined in Figure 6–1. It is becoming more and more evident that good research is done by good men. Therefore, some agencies tend to follow what they consider to be a more certain path to successful results by supporting good and proven men.

9. National security classification aspects. In the current state of world affairs research is often security classified in the interest of national defense. Therefore, it is

---

BIOGRAPHICAL SKETCH

DOKES, JOHN D.—Research Engineer, Mechanical Science Section

Education

B.S.M.E.—University A	1940
M.S.M.E.—University B	1942
Ph.D.—University C	1950

Employment History

Company A—Research Design Engineer	1942–1943
U.S. Army—Engineering Officer (Lt. to Col.)	1943–1947
Company B—Research Engineer	1947–1948
University C—Research Fellow	1948–1950
Company C—Research Scientist	1950–Present

Experience Summary: Was a research design engineer of automotive equipment. On active duty with the Army for a period of four years in an engineering capacity. Is interested in basic and applied research and has done research work on turbine cooling. Was a project director on a large project involving rotating equipment for power applications. Has several patents on turbine type equipment. Is currently a research scientist doing basic and applied research in the rotating equipment field.

Current Fields of Interest

Heat transfer; rotating equipment; mechanical design; vibrations.

Patents

1. "................" U.S. Patent No................
2. "................" U.S. Patent No................
3. "................" U.S. Patent No................

Major Reports and Publications

1. "Rotating Wheels and Centrifugal Strength" M.S. thesis, University B.
   Published in...........................1942.
2. "Turbine Dynamics and Transients" Ph.D. thesis, University C.
   Published in...........................1950.
3. "Final Reports—Contracts"................1952–1956.
4. "Journal Articles"......................1952–1962.
5. "Etc.".................................

FIG. 6–1

TYPICAL BIOGRAPHICAL SKETCH OUTLINE

important that the proposal be properly handled and labeled if it contains information which is important to national defense. (See references.)

10. Budget items and totals by yearly periods or program phases. Obviously, the total cost of the research effort should be given. A cost breakdown includes salary rates, equipment costs, travel costs, publication expenses, and other direct and indirect costs. Indirect costs are overhead expenses, etc., usually a percentage of direct salaries and wages expended on the project, to cover expenses which are not directly attributed to the project work.

11. Other federal agencies receiving the proposal. In some cases, it may be desirable to submit the proposal to more than one government agency. If this is the case, then it is ethical for the submitting organization to provide each government agency with a list of the other agencies which have received the proposal. This simplifies interagency evaluation and prevents the proposal-initiating organization from being criticized or accused of attempting to obtain support for the same project from more than one agency. This latter practice, of course, is unethical if not illegal and any indication of intent to attempt this practice should be avoided.

Many agencies of the government desire the technical and the financial aspects of the proposal to be in separate documents. The purpose for this procedure is to permit the technical part of the proposal to be evaluated without being influenced by the budget. Consequently, in such cases it is necessary to divide the proposal into two parts. Part I should be the technical and related data section and Part II should contain the administrative and financial details of the proposal.

In general it is not possible for government agencies to provide support for all of the proposals which they receive. Usually, the principal elements considered in evaluating proposals are the scientific merit of the proposal, the qualifications of the principal investigator, the significance of the planned research in reference to the requirements of the agency, and the cost of the research project. Proposals are evaluated by the professional staff of the government and, in many cases, by outstanding scientists in educational and industrial organizations. In some cases, nongovernment personnel will contribute evaluations on a no-cost or gratis basis, such as those conducted by educators for the National Science Foundation. In other cases, consultants may be retained on contract to help the government personnel make decisions in regard to the research proposals. It is usually the desire of the government agency to have a proposal e-valuated in as short a time as possible. Unfortunately, personnel and administrative problems, the large numbers of proposals received, and budgetary limitations act to delay evaluations. Consequently, it is not always possible for an evaluation of a research proposal to be obtained in less than six or seven months. This time lag makes it extremely difficult for research organizations to plan their operations.

Federal agencies generally use four types of instruments for sponsoring research. These are research grants, fixed-price contracts, cost-type contracts, and interagency fund transfers. The choice of the instrument to fund the research depends upon the nature of the research to be supported and various administrative factors.

Research grants are usually used for the support of fundamental investigations and are issued to nonprofit scientific and educational institutions. These grants, in some cases, can extend for a period of up to five years. Payments are made in advance on a periodic basis.

Fixed-price and cost-reimbursement contracts usually provide support for programs wherein the research is more of an applied or developmental nature. In these cases, more detailed planning can take place and dead-lines can be established for the courses of the investiga-tions. The fixed-price contract differs from the grant primarily in that it requires a more explicit description of the proposed program. Another difference is the method by which payments are authorized after the submission of required reports. The cost contract is usually used to support applied or developmental re-search, which has a fixed objective to be obtained in a given time period, but for which the costs cannot be accurately forecast. It is usually employed when a profit or fixed fee is charged. This type of contract anticipates a fixed fee upon a predicted cost; however, because of the nature of the work, the cost might be hard to estimate. Therefore, the government will essentially pay all the costs that are required to attain the goal set.

One of the advantages of doing research for the gov-ernment is that it is possible, in some cases, for a company or an educational institution to retain commercial patent rights on the research being conducted. Therefore, the chance exists that the research organization may secure for itself valuable assets in commercial patent rights on work which was conducted utilizing federal funds. It should be kept in mind that the government retains a royalty-free right to utilize the patents for government purposes. The institution or corporation, however, often is free to apply the patents commercially for its benefit. This is not unfair to the government, because, in many cases, prior to the presentation of the idea for remaining support by the government, the initial ideas for the work and some of the preliminary effort was funded by the contractor. In some cases, the sponsoring government agency does have a legislative requirement to assume title to any invention resulting from research which it sup-ports. This legislation, however, usually provides that the administrator of the agency may waive this restriction and assign the title of any invention back to the contractor if it is in the public interest to do so. Of course, the government retains a royalty-free license to utilize the patents obtained on the work.

It should be pointed out that for many organizations which perform most of their work on government contracts, the overhead rates which are charged on government contracts are verified by government audit agencies. This prevents educational institutions associated with nonprofit corporations from making a profit except for the intangible benefits which accrue from having a research organization associated with the educational aspects of the university. Graduate students, professors, and undergraduate students all benefit educationally and financially from the fact that they are able to work on government contracts. The government, of course, benefits greatly by getting much of its basic research done at or below cost.

Solicited Research and Development Proposals

Much of the work performed for the government under contract with companies, universities, and private research organizations contributes to satisfying the responsibilities for the national welfare which have been assigned to the various federal agencies. For instance, the Department of Defense must secure and maintain for the security of the United States of America a large, competent, well-armed and well-trained organization for defense operations. To supply this defense organization with the latest and best equipment and facilities, the Department of Defense must assure an adequate technological capability. Consequently, it solicits for proposals from external research and development organizations to provide the desired technological effort. Of course, it also must provide for production of the required supply items. The Department of Defense purchasing agents, therefore, have the responsibility of receiving bids and securing for the utilization of the Department of Defense a myriad of items which range from the bare necessities of life to the abstract items involved in new theories of gravitation, etc.

As would be expected, the types of contracts utilized to procure these items vary. For items which are readily obtainable or those which have been engineered and are now mass produced for public consumption, a fixed-price contract can be used. The government sends out invitations to companies to bid on the items it needs. Usually— but not always—the lowest bidder is awarded the contract to supply the goods. Although the lowness of the bid usually carries the greatest weight, other factors such as unique capabilities, and financial stability, will enter into the final decision. In the final analysis, the government will award the contract on the basis of the combination of factors which are to its greatest benefit.

In some cases, it may be necessary for the government to enter into developmental contracts. For instance, it may be desired to develop a new engine for a supersonic airplane. To secure the engine, the government agency will request a proposal for a development contract which will probably be funded on a cost-plus-fixed-fee basis to develop the engine according to detailed specifications. In this case, the various engine manufacturers will prepare proposals which will outline performance specifications, potential weights, etc., of their proposed engines. These proposals will be based upon the extrapolation of existing knowledge about pertinent engines and will, therefore, contain some valid foundation in fact. The proposals will then be submitted to the government and the government staff will decide which company should receive the contract to perform the required developmental work. Often, in addition to the proposal, the companies will make formal oral presentations, amplified by charts, demonstrations, etc., to the government agencies. These presentations permit clarification of questionable aspects in the proposals and help the government staff in arriving at the decision as to which proposed program to support with federal funds.

In other cases, the government may desire to sponsor research in an area in which they are experiencing difficulties on a system currently under development or for which a long-range need is forecasted. Hence, they request a proposal outlining a basic or applied research study, in the form of a *statement of work,* to supply information which is required. This type of solicitation would, in all probability, be directed to research agencies which specialize in doing the type of research required. It would not necessarily be directed mainly to companies which might have an interest in supplying the complete or final system to the federal government.

Because the government does solicit for research and development work, it is important that any company or research organization file its capabilities with the various government agencies which initiate contracts. This will assure that the company will be considered when proposals are solicited.

Industry Sponsored Research

Whereas it is normal operating procedure for a lengthy period of time to elapse before a proposal submitted to a government agency is finally acted upon, it is customary for work required by industrial sponsors to be handled at a much more rapid rate. This is easily explained by the fact that industrial sponsors need research results in order to make money. Time, as indicated in Chapter 4, often can be the equivalent of money. Therefore, the industrial sponsor must expedite paper work not only to get the research done but also to save as much money as possible, and it can be assumed that if sponsorship or consideration of a proposal is not fairly rapid the work will not be supported.

Unsolicited Industrial Research

If a research organization has a process or product which it feels has a commercial potential, it may approach an industrial firm with a research proposal with hopes of getting support for research work to develop the process or product. This proposal is called an *unsolicited industrial proposal.*

Industry is not apt to support unsolicited marginal or low-probability-of-success work. Industrial firms are anxious to make money and will, therefore, look very carefully into the potentials of a possible process or product before they will invest money in its support. If industry does support research work which is of an unsolicited nature, they will usually retain all or most of the patent rights to any process or product which is generated or developed with their money.

A typical research industrial agreement form used by a nonprofit research corporation is given in Figure 6–2. This agreement form is of the cost-reimbursement type. It assures that the research organization, which is proposing to perform the work, will not take a loss even though the project may be unsuccessful. The agreement form, in paragraphs 8 and 9, gives to the sponsor all the patent rights to the products of the research effort.

AGREEMENT FOR INDUSTRIAL RESEARCH PROJECT

Date ...... ,. ....

Research Project No. ....

THIS AGREEMENT, made and entered into this .... day of .... 19....,

between   Research Institute, a corporation of   , of the city of   ,

hereinafter known as "Institute," and ....

a corporation duly organized and existing under the laws of the State of ....,

having an office and place of business in ...., hereinafter
known as the "Second Party," witnesseth that:

WHEREAS one of the purposes of the Institute is to engage in scientific research, and,

WHEREAS the Second Party believes that its business interests will be advanced by this
agreement considering the benefits reasonably to be expected by it,

THEREFORE, for the purpose of promoting the increase of useful knowledge, and in
consideration of the mutual promises and covenants herein contained, the parties hereto
agree as follows:

1. As used in this agreement, it is understood that the words "research project" or "project" shall refer to the subject of the scientific investigation covered by this agreement, which shall be identified in the files of the Institute as "Research Project No. ...."; the words "staff member" shall mean persons on the technical or scientific staff of the Institute, or assistants or employees, who shall be engaged in the work on this research project.

2. The Second Party hereby engages the Institute to carry on research and development work for the Second Party relating to Research Project No. .... and specifically defined in addendum to this agreement of the same date and identified as "addendum to Research Project No. ....," for a period of .... commencing on the day that staff assignments to the project are made. The Institute shall perform this research project at its laboratories or otherwise, and shall provide the project with all its available equipment and laboratory and shop facilities.

3. In the event that experimental plant work shall be recommended by the President of the Institute and approved by the Second Party, the necessary plant facilities of the Second Party shall be made available to the Institute without charge. Shop facilities of the Second Party shall be available for use of the Institute without charge when recommended by the President of the Institute and approved by the Second Party.

4. The Second Party agrees to pay to the Institute, and the Institute agrees to charge the Second Party, for the work on this project, on the following basis:

   (a) The actual sum of money paid by the Institute as compensation to its staff members or agents employed by it on this research project including part time services which shall be prorated; plus

   (b) 100% of the sum of money paid by the Institute under (a) to the staff members and agents employed by it on this research project (to cover overhead, etc., not directly chargeable to a project) ; plus

   (c) Special equipment, supplies and patent costs, traveling and other incidental expenses directly chargeable to this project.

FIG. 6–2

INDUSTRIAL RESEARCH AGREEMENT FORM

5. The Institute will render when work on the project commences a bill to cover the estimate of cost of this project for its first month which the Second Party will pay. Thereafter the Institute will render its invoices on or about the first of each month covering the previous months actual cost chargeable to the Second Party. The Second Party agrees to pay the invoices of the Institute so rendered on or before the fifteenth day of each month. The amount advanced by the Second Party to cover the estimate of cost for the first month shall be deducted by the Institute from its invoices covering completion of the project.

6. The Second Party agrees to appropriate a total sum not to exceed................... .... Dollars for this project, and the Institute shall not expend more than said sum without first securing the specific written approval of the Second Party to do so. The Institute reserves the right to discontinue work on this project if the Second Party fails to pay invoices rendered by the Institute within the time herein specified.

7. At the end of each calendar month during the term of the project the Institute agrees to render to the Second Party a brief, condensed, written report of its findings and progress, in duplicate.

8. Any and all patentable inventions, applications for patent and patents thereon relating to the subject matter of the project as herein defined which may be hereafter made by staff members or agents employed by the Institute on this project, during the time they are performing work on this project and as a result thereof, shall become the property of the Second Party, subject to the terms and conditions of this agreement. The Institute agrees to require every staff member and agent employed by it to execute and deliver to the Institute an agreement whereby inventions, coming under the terms hereof, shall belong to and become the property of the Institute. Should a staff member or agent refuse to assign to the Institute any invention coming under the terms hereof, the Institute agrees to assign its interest to said invention to the Second Party so that the Second Party may take such steps as it deems advisable to compel said staff member or agent to specifically perform his contract. The Institute shall cause to be kept complete and systematic memoranda in writing, including notes on all experimental and research work, descriptions, diagrams and other data, pertaining to inventions relating to said subject made while working on said project and resulting from work on said research project, which memoranda shall be available at all times to the Second Party.

9. Upon request and at the expense of the Second Party, the Institute agrees to use its best efforts to cause its staff members and agents to execute all necessary papers to make application for letters patent of the United States and of all foreign countries and to convey complete title to the Second Party to the inventions defined in the preceding paragraph. In the event the Second Party desires to keep secret any new process, device, machine, or composition of matter, invented by the project, relating to the project, invented by staff members or agents employed on this project and as a result of their work thereon, the Institute shall use its best efforts to maintain the said secret and not to disclose the same to anyone without the consent of the Second Party.

10. In the event of any difference of opinion between the parties hereto as to the interpretation or performance of this agreement, or the rights of the respective parties to this agreement, the matters in issue shall be referred to a Board of Arbitration, which Board shall consist of a representative of the Institute and a representative of the Second Party and a third person whom these two shall select. In the event of failure

FIG. 6–2 (Cont.)

INDUSTRIAL RESEARCH AGREEMENT FORM

of the two arbitrators to agree upon the third arbitrator, aforementioned, the third arbitrator shall be named by American Arbitration Association. The decision of a majority of this Board shall be final and binding upon the parties hereto and pending the action of said Board no suit shall be brought by either party; provided that if the parties refuse to arbitrate, then neither party shall bring suit against the other in any court until a period of three (3) months has elapsed from the date a dispute arose between the parties. In the event the parties are unable to amicably adjust their differences within three (3) months from the date the dispute arose between them, then, and in that event, the parties agree that a suit based upon said dispute must be brought within six (6) months from the date such dispute arose, and if a suit is not filed within said period, the parties agree that they shall forever be barred from maintaining any action based upon said dispute.

11. It is also agreed that no advertising or publicity matter having or containing any reference to the   Research Institute or in which the name is mentioned, shall be made use of by the Second Party or anyone in the Second Party's behalf unless and until the same shall have first been submitted to and received the approval of the Institute.

12. Neither party shall make any claim against the other for damages or for other relief based upon the failure of either party to observe any condition herein made binding in the event such failure is caused by reason of the fact that the party in default complied with any law, rule or regulation of the United States Government or of the State of   , or if such failure is due to any cause beyond the control of the party in default.

13. The Institute agrees that it will not conduct investigations relating to this project for any other person during the period it is performing work on this project.

14. Realizing the value of teaching practice to a scientist who is conducting research work, it is understood that any scientist, assistant, or employee of the Institute, although assigned to this project may spend not to exceed two hours per day in the pursuit of teaching, without such teaching time being deducted from the time otherwise properly chargeable against the project.

15. In the event the project sum is expended prior to the expiration of this agreement, then this project shall terminate unless the Second Party in writing authorizes the Institute to continue this project.

IN WITNESS WHEREOF, the parties hereto have caused this agreement to be duly executed by their duly authorized officers the day and year first above written.

RESEARCH INSTITUTE

BY ....

BY ....

SECOND PARTY

....
Name

BY ....

BY ....

FIG. 6–2 (Cont.)

Industrial Research Agreement Form

Unsolicited industrial support for basic research is usually difficult to obtain, as compared to federal sponsorship. Consequently, unsolicited basic research work is usually proposed to government agencies where the probability of support is greater. A progressive independent research organization, however, will try to maintain a balance between government and industrial sponsorship. It seems that the effort to obtain unsolicited support from industry is not pursued as much as it should be by various organizations in the growing research and development business.

Solicited Industrial Research

If a company has a problem which it cannot solve with its own research organization, or if it is too small to have a satisfactory research effort, then it may wish to sponsor a research project at a research institution, private R and D company, or university. The company, in this manner, solicits industrial research and, consequently, any research program which a research organization responsively submits to the company is called a *solicited industrial proposal.*

If the proposal is accepted, the research organization initiates a research effort to solve the problem posed. To maintain a good sponsor relationship, the difference between production costs and research costs should be pointed out to the sponsor at every opportunity. In general, production costs are low compared to the value of the item produced. Research costs on the other hand are high and the item produced may be only a small written report. This report may contain much valuable information; however, considerable time and effort are usually required before this information becomes a tangible profit. An expenditure of $10,000 by an industrial concern can easily buy a new lathe, a new milling machine, or a specialized piece of industrial equipment. This equipment almost immediately begins to generate a profit. The same $10,000 may buy only a twenty-page research report which may take many additional thousands of dollars to implement into practical production profits.

Another aspect of research which should be pointed out to the uninformed sponsor is that research is not a *sure thing*. Perhaps nine out of ten research efforts will not result in commercially valuable processes or products. However, in the specific one case where successful results are obtained, the effort repays, many times over, all the unsuccessful efforts which have gone before. The unfortunate fact here is that many small companies are not able to support several different projects. If they are unfortunate enough to support only a few low-yield projects, then before long they will be out of business or, at least, disgusted with research. If, however, a small company is fortunate enough to support a high-yield project effort, then it may soon grow into a large company on the basis of the results from the research. It is self-evident, therefore, that all industrial research investments should be made only after due deliberation and the application of as much sound judgment as possible.

Proposals for Company-Funded Internal Research

Company research organizations are usually not exempt from the preparation of proposals for research programs they desire to initiate. As a matter of fact, most companies have very small total budgets for research effort, and potential programs are reviewed very carefully before they receive any of these precious dollars. Again, the impression the proposed program creates in the minds of the reviewers is directly dependent upon the proposal. The proposal must sell the attractiveness of the research venture without false representation and with little need for follow-up explanation. The reviewer tends to regard any hedging or obvious omission of information as an attempt to cover up unattractive aspects of the program.

Proposals for company funds to support in-house research efforts differ from those discussed in previous sections of this chapter principally in the additional economic considerations that must be included. A format similar to that provided in Figure 6–3 is suggested for use

---

Title Page—Descriptive title for project; starting and estimated completion dates; principal investigator
1. Technical objective
2. Technical discussion, approach, and scope (include breakdown into phases)
3. Company objectives and product areas affected
4. Significant previous efforts
5. Estimated requirements (by phases):
   a. Man-power and personnel costs
   b. Materials and supplies
   c. Major facilities required
   d. Travel and miscellaneous costs
   e. Estimated budget summary
6. Chart of major milestones (by month or week)
7. Chart of cost spread (by month or week)
8. Estimated primary and secondary benefits to company
9. Concluding Remarks (including chances of project success)

FIG. 6–3

TYPICAL FORMAT FOR PROPOSAL RELATING TO AN INTERNALLY FUNDED INDUSTRIAL RESEARCH PROJECT

on internal proposals. The specific items in the figure can be altered to meet the requirements of almost any type of company.

Selling R and D Proposals

Up to this point, little has been said about sales effort. Some corporations that are deeply involved in government contract research and development work have very competent and active sales groups. These groups encourage the technical people to produce ideas and then prepare proposals in such form that a very salable offering results. They usually maintain offices in the Washington, D.C. area, and also near various other government installations. In general, they keep their fingers on the research pulse of the government.

Such companies use the hard-sell approach to obtaining research and development funds. In some cases, they tend to mold research programs through the advanced thinking of their staffs in areas in which the government is interested. They push research and development and attempt to lead government planning. Other agencies, including some educational nonprofit institutions, do not use hard-sell techniques. They submit proposals, of course, but they do not push the proposals in the sense that a salesman would. They attempt to let the proposals sell themselves, hoping that good work will sell itself. This is not always true; however, if a reputation is established by a research organization for superior work, then, to a large extent, the proposals do sell themselves, and little outside sales effort is required.

It is interesting to note how one educational institution went about selling a research proposal to a government agency. This institution has a large research experiment station which is of the typical nonprofit type. A professor in one of the educational departments of the university was interested in doing a piece of research on an internal combustion engine. A research administrator in the engineering experiment station whom he approached thought the idea seemed to offer much promise of a better engine with improved performance. As a consequence, they made a trip to a government agency to determine whether or not any interest could be aroused in support of the basic idea. As stated before, government agencies are very courteous and will give a hearing to almost any idea proposed. Fortunately, this idea was well received and the proper government channel in which to place a research proposal for it was delineated to the research administrator and the professor. After the professor prepared the technical data on his idea and the research administrator prepared the proper forms, including budgets, time, and contractual procedures, the proposal was submitted to the proper government agency. This agency was visited and the proposal details were discussed with the government's technical representatives. These representatives felt that the proposal was one which would offer substantial benefits to the overall government vehicle program and, consequently, they were anxious to support the work. They assured the research administrator and the professor that they would support the work and that notification of the awarding of a contract would be received in due time. After approximately six months of waiting, the contract was awarded. It was a cost-reimbursement type which permitted the professor to hire students for the work and to start the project. The end result expected by the university is a more competent professor because of the work, and possibly commercial benefits from inventions developed on the contract. The government will obtain engines which should materially decrease its problem of logistic support to the armed forces.

In research as in other operations, *nothing succeeds like success.* If an organization has a successful record in the performance of research and development in the past, and if it has well-known nationally famous scientists on its staff, then research opportunities will be presented to it for its acceptance. In other words, the old saying, *If you make a better mousetrap, the world will beat a path to your door,* is true for research. If you have a good research success story behind you, the agencies desiring research will beat a path to your door. Therefore, this gives another rule which should be kept in mind.

Successful research breeds new research; research failures breed sterility and decline.

Summary

Research is like any other product in that it must be sold. The selling of a research effort is usually initiated by formalizing the program of work into a written proposal. Because positive research results cannot be guaranteed, it is usually unwise for a research organization to guarantee results in a proposal. The proposal, however, should completely describe the proposed program and the ideas on which the program is based. An important question the writer of a proposal should ask himself is, *"Does this proposal give all the information necessary to indicate to the reader the purpose of the proposed research program?"* Another important question is, *"Does this proposal anticipate answers to questions which an intelligent reader would logically be expected to ask?"*

One primary source of research funds at present is the federal government. The magnitude of the technological requirements of the nation are such that the government will sponsor good work in almost any discipline. Of course, it is important to realize the areas which are currently receiving emphasis. The Department of Defense and the National Aeronautics and Space Administration are two government agencies which have large research budgets.

In writing proposals for submission to the government, it is important that the proposal be as explicit as possible in reference to the research objectives, money and time required, cost basis, and personnel to be assigned to the work. It is also important to clearly indicate the name of the organization submitting the proposal and whether or not the proposal is being submitted for consideration by other agencies.

Research work is supported under various types of grants and contracts. The contracts may be of the fixed-price type and have incentive, firm, escalation, and redetermination bases. They may also be of the cost-reimbursement type and have fixed fee, incentive fee, and no fee bases. In basic and applied research endeavor, care should be taken to obtain contractual agreements which will not require the contractor to produce tightly specified results, since research, in itself, cannot be guaranteed. The contract can and should, however, require that a diligent effort be expended in accordance with that specified in the proposal.

Industrial sponsored research may be of the solicited or unsolicited type. In some cases it may be funded and performed completely within the company and is then termed company-funded internal research.

Sales effort for research and development proposals varies. Some organizations use the *hard-sell* and push research with aggressive sales organizations; others use the *soft-sell* and let their proposals sell themselves. A middle course is probably preferable for most organizations. Successful research performance in the past, with a modest amount of promotional effort, will assure that good ideas and programs will be well received and will, for the most part, be supported.

Chapter 7

Conducting the Research and Development Project

WHEN a research project has been activated, it is necessary that the work be done in the most efficient and expeditious manner possible. It is important, therefore, for the research organization to assign responsibility for the research and development project to an individual who is scientifically competent, mature, reliable, willing to work hard, and who understands the meaning of time and money. If a research project is the responsibility of an individual who does not have these characteristics, then it can be expected that the project will have an unsuccessful conclusion. Even if the work is satisfactory, in all probability, the money will be overexpended, and the contract time exceeded. If a project is unsuccessful it will usually be found that the reason lies in the misuse of the men, money, and time available.

In the above it was assumed, of course, that the research project had been well planned, satisfactorily budgeted, and had a solution. It should be pointed out that the success of a research program is not always determined by whether or not a successful experimental demonstration of a hypothesis is achieved. In fact, many of the research and development projects which are considered successful by research organizations do not have as their end results successful processes or solutions. They have, however, by proper allocation of people, money, and time, resulted in intelligent conclusions from the efforts, which when documented in technical reports delineate what was found, give the methods of procedure which were used to determine the findings, and give recommendations which will be useful in the future.

Programming of the Research and Development Project

When a project director is assigned to a project, one of his first steps should be to set up funds for various phases of the work. He should examine the project's goals very carefully, determine what technically talented individuals he has available to complete the work satisfactorily, and allocate various time periods for different phases of the project. Of course, it is realized that the money which is available will to a large extent determine the number and, in some cases, the types of personnel which can be employed on the project. Generally, it is necessary and desirable to utilize the organization's own personnel and upon whom the work that was proposed was predicated. It is very important for the project director to establish his budgets and authorize personnel for his project as rapidly as possible so that the work will not be unduly delayed and personnel lost to other company assignments.

After the budget and personnel requirements are met, the project director should establish important milestones for the research effort. Milestones are important accomplishments necessary for the success of the project. They should be noted together with the date at which these steps should normally be completed. If a milestone record is kept, the project director can at any time determine whether or not the project is progressing satisfactorily. "Critical Path Diagramming," "Project

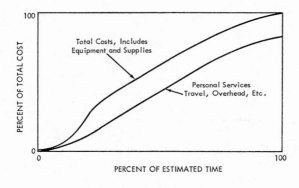

FIG. 7–1

PROJECT EXPENDITURES VERSUS TIME

Planning and Evaluation," and "PERT" (Program Evaluation and Review Technique) are modern variations, using mathematical tools, etc., for maintaining a good milestone record. (See references for this chapter.) These methods should be studied in detail by persons responsible for maintaining the milestone report records. The money expenditures for a project can normally be expected, if plotted against time, to form an S-curve similar to that shown in Figure 7–1. As would be expected the initial expenditure rate starts out slowly. Then it increases to a constant value. Finally, near the end of the project, it tapers off. Of course, if large equipment costs are incurred these will usually be superimposed on the S-curve and, consequently, distort it by the amount of the capital encumbered. Parallel to the money curve should be plotted a manpower plus milestone graph. A typical plot is shown in Figure 7–2. This figure also indicates the S-type curve which characterizes the expenditure curve for the project.

Another important responsibility of the project director is to establish and maintain good sponsor relation-

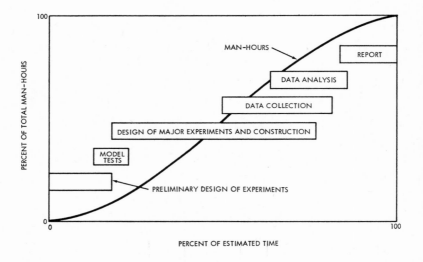

FIG. 7–2

PROJECT MANPOWER AND MILESTONE EFFORT VERSUS TIME

ships. Complete periodic progress reports are one of the best methods for accomplishing this aim. Progress reports should not be considered as a chore, but as having a twofold value. A good project report will state what is being done, how the money is being expended, what breakthroughs have been made, and what progress is planned for the next report period. In submitting progress reports, therefore, the project director satisfies himself that things are going along as scheduled, as well as keeping his sponsor informed as to the status of the work. Even if the progress reports are negative and pessimistic, it is important that they be forwarded promptly and that they represent as accurately as possible the project status. Accurate reports will reflect upon the integrity of the organization and the sponsor will respect the project director and the organization for their reliability. If a project director misrepresents the status of the work, this for a short time may permit him an easier situation; however, when the project time has been consumed and the money expended, he will suffer a more drastic penalty—*he may lose his job.*

As stated before, many projects do not arrive at successful conclusions. In some cases, negative results will be reported. If, however, the reports are accurate and factual and indicate that the money was spent as wisely as possible, then no discredit should accrue to the project director and to his organization.

Personnel Assignments

The project director or project manager is a very important individual and his contribution to the success of a research organization cannot be overstated. It was indicated before that the project should be placed in the hands of an individual who is scientifically competent, mature, reliable, willing to work hard, and who understands the meaning of time and money. The project director should also be an individual whose mind is continually searching for new ideas. He should have the curiosity of the creative individual; however, he need not himself be extremely creative. He should accept new ideas readily if they are good. He should as easily reject new ideas if they have no worth. The project director, in other words, should serve as a filter to sift information coming into the project and reject or accept it as necessary. Of course, it is realized that in large projects he will be unable to make all of the detailed technical decisions because of the many complex systems and disciplines which are involved. In these cases the project director should be willing to delegate authority and responsibility to his staff.

A good project director is one who expects his project personnel to carry out orders without quibbling. At the same time he is an individual who accepts advice from his subordinates and expects them to give this advice freely with no fear of retaliation if the advice is contrary to what he wants to hear. He should, however, expect orders once given to be followed and obeyed without delay. He should be an individual who is strong enough to see that the orders are obeyed, and he should be forceful enough to use sufficient punishment, dismissal or otherwise, if his orders are not obeyed. He should also be magnanimous enough to use only enough punishment to assure that an offense is not repeated. He should give loyalty to his superiors and should expect loyalty from his subordinates.

A good project director will remember that sins of omission can be greater than sins of commission. He will expect his people to turn out work, and will not tolerate indolence or ineffectiveness.

A good project director should give credit where credit is due. He should not grab all the credit for himself. He should know that if his organization is good he will get the credit for the operation.

A good project director should clearly set forth the responsibilities of every man in his organization. He should be positive about these responsibilities. He should let his staff know what the consequences of failure to live up to responsibility will be; however, he should not bluff or threaten them. He should know his men as personally as possible, but he should not enter into factions or cliques. He should make each man in his organization feel free to discuss personal matters with him. However, he should not tolerate breaking the chain of command in the organization. While he should assume that his men do their own jobs, it is his responsibility to see that the jobs are done properly. He should encourage his personnel to inspect their work constantly to see that they are performing properly and to the utmost of their ability. A staff inspector might assist in this function, but ultimately he must see for himself what is going on.

The above characteristics are those required for project managers and for supervisors of large groups of individuals. The next lower step in the chain of command is the project engineer. The requirements of a project engineer are not quite as stringent as those required for a project manager. The project engineer should keep his mind open to new ideas and he should be, if possible, more creative than even the project manager. The project engineer, in some cases, may work with large groups; in others he may work by himself. If the project engineer is in charge of a section or group of individuals then the characteristics of the project manager, on a somewhat reduced scale in magnitude, are applicable to him.

Since the project engineer is a project manager on a reduced scale, it is logical for an expanding organization to obtain project managers from project engineers who have demonstrated their ability to delegate authority and handle large numbers of men. If a project engineer desires to do only technical work and gets a great sense of satisfaction from doing a good technical job, this characteristic will probably prevent him from going up the promotional ladder in the organization to project manager, division director, general manager, etc. This desire, however, should not be decried. A project engineer who is content to do technical jobs well is a very important man to an organization. He is usually well educated, well informed in his field of specialty, and is an authority on whom the project director, etc., can depend to assure that the technical performance on the research project is satisfactory. His promotional and salary growth avenues should be kept as professionally rewarding as are those for research management.

The Investigative Procedure

The researcher continually faces the problem of obtaining answers to little-known phenomena. There are, in general, two methods of solving a problem: the experimental method and the analytical method. It will usually be found that defining the problem is the first and most important step in either method. If the researcher can think out the problem clearly, decide what is desired, and place a reasonable estimate on the accuracy of the various components, then he is well on the way to a solution. Inexperienced researchers will probably desire, in their solutions, to maintain accuracies all out of proportion to the necessary or potentially attainable final results. The imposition of stringent numerical accuracy, as for instance, a fraction of 1 percent, when the assumptions fed into the solution are too inadequate to justify such accuracy, is foolish. The mark of a seasoned researcher is his knowledge of what can be obtained and what can readily be accomplished within the bounds of the assumptions and investigative techniques he employs. This does not mean that sloppy calculations can be tolerated;

rather, it means that judicious logic and reasoning should be used to place an intelligent limit or bound upon the answers to be obtained.

The experimental method of solving problems implies familiarity with similar systems. A similar system may be a part of a whole which is to be analyzed; as for instance, one tube out of a heat exchanger that consists of many tubes. If the one tube is experimentally examined, at a much reduced cost, then the performance of a large number of similar tubes can be accurately ascertained. The use of models is another technique of the experimental method of solving problems. Models are constructed for which similarity of behavior with that of the proposed apparatus is assured. For instance, small models of aircraft are built and tested in wind tunnels prior to the building of the actual plane resulting in savings in time and money. The method of models is satisfactory because experience has indicated that definite relationships exist between the model results and the operation of the full-scale system. The experimental method of solving problems, therefore, can be either that of similarity or the method of models.

In solving problems by the analytical method, some experimental experience is usually necessary. Familiarity with the behavior of the actual system is a requisite, even though it may be necessary to idealize the system for computational simplicity or because of lack of knowledge. In this idealization of the system, the danger of introducing errors of large magnitude is great. A veteran researcher with a vast amount of experience is generally in a much better position to idealize an actual system than is the neophyte. Despite the fact that the analytical solution of a problem describes the performance of the system under consideration, the result is no more representative of the actual system than the assumptions that were introduced. If the assumptions describe the actual system precisely, then the analytical solution will describe the behavior of the actual system precisely. If the assumptions are in error by a significant factor, then the answer can be in error by a large amount.

The analytical attack on a problem yields, therefore, a theoretically predicted result; the experimental attack on a problem yields the empirical or measured result. Most engineering problems in practice find their way to the laboratory and are experimentally solved; however, the solution is not usually considered complete until a corresponding analytical answer for the problem is obtained. A complete analysis of the problem generally permits intelligent extrapolation of the results to new or somewhat different situations.

The experimental method of models may sometimes be extrapolated to other systems by analogy, or the use of analogues. For instance, in heat transfer it is found that many of the heat conduction problems can be considered to be analogous to electrical conduction problems. Temperature can be the analogue of voltage and heat flow the analogue of electric current. If the idealized systems of two different types of problems, for instance the heat flow problem and the electrical problem, have similar differential equations and if the boundary and initial conditions are similar, then a change of variables will transform the equations of one system into those of the other. By this method it is possible to solve a problem in heat transfer by using an electrical model or, in other words, an electrical analogue.

In general, a research and development project involves the solution of many individual problems. These problems have individual solutions which take place in a sequence of events. First, the problem must be defined or idealized. Second, an attempt must be made to solve the idealized problem by either or both of the two methods discussed. If the problem is clearly defined, the solution will usually be straightforward and will result in relationships which have physical significance.

Tools and Research

Research tools include instruments, machines, and facilities for the accomplishment of the research and development task. Tools for research, therefore, may be as small as a paper and pencil or as large as a complex nuclear reactor. They may cost a few pennies or many millions of dollars.

From the stone age to our modern atomic or space age, it has been the development of power sources and tools which has permitted man to improve his standard of living. Through the development of electric power generators and motors, utilizing thermal or atomic energy as prime power sources, human slavery has almost disappeared. It has become cheaper to do physical work with machines rather than with humans. In addition, computing machines are being used more and more for routine thinking tasks and soon it may become cheaper to use machines for most of these routine operations. Nevertheless, man still has a place because of his ability to think. The sequence of events for the developments discussed above is as follows:

1. Machines eliminate human slavery by doing civilization's work more economically.
2. Computers eliminate intellectual drudgery by accomplishing complex analytical tasks more efficiently and economically.

3. Time becomes available to all for creative pursuits. Physical work and mental drudgery become less necessary to sustain a standard of living.

Transportation wonders have also evolved through improvements in tools and methods of analysis. The old wooden airplane that was held together with wire and prayers is now the large modern jet airliner. Tools of construction (lathes, milling machines, etc.) and tools for material processing (Bessemer convertors, open-hearth and electric furnaces, ore fluidization processes, etc.) have all contributed much to the progress of mankind. The various advances, in many cases, are interdependent. Today, civilization rests on a broad base of technical information, technological know-how, capital equipment, communication and transportation systems, and power sources. Without this base the researcher could do little. It is interesting to compare modern western civilization with some of the backward civilizations on the earth. In the United States if a person desires anything from a nail to a complex production machine, all he needs to do, if he has the necessary money, is to telephone or write an order for the item wanted. In a relatively short time he has what he wants. However, if a person in a relatively undeveloped country desires even such a small item as a nut or bolt, he may have to wait months before it can be transported in from the United States or some similarly developed country. The fact that an excellent distribution system exists in the U.S. makes every part of the country almost like any other. Ease of transportation, good communication systems, good educational systems, and a stable government can also be considered as basic ingredients of sophisticated research and development.

One tool of research which has become very prominent

in the last decade is the nuclear research reactor. These reactors, which utilize the fission of Uranium 235 to create high neutron fluxes and very intense gamma radiation, are extremely expensive. For instance, a small research reactor and associated facilities will cost about $4,500,000. Therefore, it is easy to understand why research can be very costly in certain sophisticated areas.

While the funds for research facilities must ultimately come from the people, the result of judicious investments in research facilities will be an improvement in the lot of everyone. Successful research will do much to improve medical treatment, materials, efficiency of production, etc. Without a continual advance or improvement in the efficiency of producing the necessities of life, civilization would soon stagnate and degenerate with time. This degeneration would take place because of an ever increasing population and the using up of rich natural resources. Up to the present time, through research, enormous quantities of natural resources and materials have been made available. These resources will not last indefinitely and must be replaced when they are exhausted. For instance, as fossil fuel is used up, mankind's power requirements must be met from other sources. Perhaps nuclear power, which is one of the latest research breakthroughs, will fill this future gap even before it exists. If the fusion process can be made to work on a controlled basis, then an unlimited power source will become available. On the basis of past experience it can be expected that the fusion problem will be solved.

In addition to supporting large research tools like nuclear reactors, the public will be called upon, through taxation, to fund other large, important research efforts. For instance, the space program will continue to consume enormous amounts of money and manpower. Although the aerospace industries will make the direct contribution of facilities and personnel to the project, everyone in the country will be touched by the effort. As to results from the program, it is apparent already that the utilization of space is a foregone conclusion. Many useful satellites are already circling the earth. Men will get to the moon; men will then visit the planets in the solar system. The enormous potential in new ideas and materials of the space program is almost beyond imagination.

In the foregoing, the discussion has revolved about large complex research tools. In addition to these large tools, there are many smaller research necessities. For instance, the ordinary slide rule is a research tool. Without it most engineers and researchers would be severely handicapped. It is a simple hand tool which gives them the ability to make rapid calculations. The slide rule, therefore, is a small research tool and costs perhaps fifteen to twenty dollars. Between the nuclear research reactor costing millions of dollars and the slide rule, the researcher uses an extremely wide variety of tools. Large wind tunnels of various types are used to determine aerodynamic heating and aerodynamic effects on aerospace systems. Smaller wind tunnels are used to determine fundamental boundary layer properties. In physics, in addition to nuclear reactors, X-ray diffraction equipment, radiation measuring instruments, and many other tools are used. Heat transfer laboratories are equipped with potentiometers and thermocouples, flow measuring devices, pressure meters, and many other instruments for use on fluid flow and heat transfer problems. Internal combustion laboratories have exhaust gas analyzers, carburetor flow metering devices, pressure sensing devices, stroboscopes, speed indicators, dynamometers, and many other devices for determining the operating characteristics of internal combustion engines. Any field that is considered has a current base of research tools which are accepted and commonplace. Without tools progress cannot be made. Tools, which are the means by which things are accomplished, are one of the most important assets of a good research organization. They do not supplant brains; however, without the proper tools, little can be done by even the most creative individual.

Some persons question the expenditure of vast sums of money for research equipment. They begrudge the fact that it costs thousands of dollars for a research instrument that is not used on even a continuous 8-hour-per-day basis. They feel that with a new lathe, they could increase production and make money for the company; consequently, they want to put all available capital into production equipment. Expenditures for research tools should never be judged or justified on the basis of an immediate economic return; rather, overall research objectives should be considered.

Summary

In this chapter the characteristics of project managers and project engineers were discussed. It was pointed out that the project manager is one of the most important persons in the successful handling and performance of a research project. A project manager should be an above-average individual. In fact, he is, if he is successful, a good budget manager and a creative, industrious, intelligent, and logical individual.

The programming of a research project was discussed and it is important to note that it involves two important aspects: (1) the anticipated rate of expenditure, and (2) the manpower and milestone report. After properly organizing and establishing the research project, the project manager utilizes these two key items to determine whether the project is on schedule and if the expenditures and the important aspects of the project are occurring in their proper and logical time sequence.

Tools and their role in research were discussed. The tools for research are vitally necessary. They range from multimillion dollar complex systems to simple numerical calculators. Perhaps the most simple tool of a researcher is a pencil and paper. Utilizing these two items it may be possible to create ideas and new processes; however, a technological base is required to bring these ideas to fruition.

Two methods for solving research problems, the analytical and the experimental or empirical, were discussed. Both of these methods have an important bearing on the successful completion of research projects. The empirical method is that utilized to obtain answers as rapidly as possible. However, the empirical method is not entirely satisfactory since empirical results usually cannot be extrapolated to new systems without some analytical verification. It was pointed out that detailed analytical calculations are only as valid as the assumptions on which they are based. In general, the conduct of a research project is a complex and complicated process. The project manager is an important individual; the project engineer also has an important place in the project; and the research tools, which the researcher will require, are vitally necessary.

Successful research, then, depends on good people, good planning, and capital equipment in the form of research tools.

Chapter 8

Reporting
Research and Development
Results

THE PROJECT MANAGER or principal investigator has set up his project, done some research, and has assembled research data. It is now required that he submit a progress report on his work. Progress reports indicate what was done, how it was accomplished, how much money was spent, who worked on the project, and what will be accomplished in the next reporting period. Although the researcher may think them a necessary evil and thus keep putting them off, they should be submitted on time. Promptness will help assure a good reputation for the research organization. The complexity of business administration makes it necessary for contracting officers to set up procedures for monitoring the work. These procedures are such that the time a report is submitted is sometimes more important contractually than its contents. An old trite saying that, "the value of a report is directly proportional to its weight" is not true; however, if it were modified to, "The value of a report to the organization is directly proportional to its contents and the promptness with which it was submitted" it would represent fact.

Progress reports may be of several forms. Some sponsors require letter reports on a monthly basis, others require quarterly reports, and some require both types. Whatever the sponsor desires will determine what is to be submitted. It should be kept in mind that the sponsor is paying the bills and, therefore, his wishes should be satisfied. Often, research and development men lose sight of the fact that it takes money to support their efforts. They sometimes get enamoured with their work and believe that they are doing the sponsors a favor by working for them. If this attitude is prevalent in a research organization it is not long before progress reports become impositions to the researcher, coffee breaks do not, and the reporting effort on projects declines into haphazard chaos. At this time, it is necessary for the research and development administrators to bring the researchers back into line. Researchers are rarely sufficiently brilliant to permit them the license of freedom from the necessary paper work entailed in reports, budgets, etc. In fact, the unusually talented person can be depended upon to do what his job requires of him. It is usually the marginally effective researcher who takes a day complaining about a report which could have been written in a few hours.

How does the research administrator make sure that the reports are written on time? The best way to assure compliance with requirements, is to employ reliable scientists and engineers. The administrator should make clear to the research personnel that prompt attention to reports will be expected of them, and that their future advancement will be hampered by faulty or late reporting. An illustrative case history concerns a researcher in a large organization who was continually late in submitting his reports. He did good work but just couldn't get around to writing reports on it. After a period of time, the sponsor became unhappy and visited the research organization and read the so-called "riot act" to the whole organization. For a short time thereafter, reports were submitted on time. Then the old cycle of delay was reinstituted. The administrators by continually needling the researcher could get out the work. This, however, took an undue amount of time and it rapidly became evident that the solution to the problem was to eliminate the individual from the organization. This example points out the importance of selecting reliable and conscientious people to serve as principal investigators.

The writing of a final report on a research or development project is probably the most important aspect of the project director's work. The report can significantly affect the reputation of the author and his organization. Although most research will generate results which are not outstanding, occasionally a project will be completed which will have an immense impact on the technological community. These projects are extremely valuable and should be exploited to their limit for the benefit of the whole research organization. The majority of the work accomplished will, however, have little immediate effect and will become a part of the reservoir of technological experience. Reports not published in recognized journals may or may not be lost to the technical community depending on whether or not they are incorporated into textbooks, journal articles, etc.

In addition to the research projects which produce breakthroughs or add to our technological reservoir, some research projects show no significant results. If, in these cases, the project director realizes the importance of properly documenting and reporting upon his labors, then the project need not be considered a failure by the research organization. As has been stated many times in this text, research by its very nature is an exploratory type of venture. Therefore, every project cannot be expected to result in new discoveries, new processes, and major technological breakthroughs. The project director on an unsuccessful project should use sound reporting techniques to document his work. The report should be factual, interesting to read, and should document in detail the avenues of research explored. The completeness of the report will indicate to the sponsors that they received value for the money expended even though the value can only be measured in the man-hours and the materials and capital consumed.

A good project manager, therefore, can create a satisfactory report on negative results. This is not to be construed to mean that a project should be initiated with the hope of having negative results. Rather it indicates that there is a technique for making a research failure a partial success. This technique involves the use of hard work, truthfulness, and integrity. The hard work comes in writing a report on something which has been disappointing and doing a good job of it. The truthfulness comes in explaining exactly what was done and analyzing the reasons for the lack of success. The integrity comes in admitting that negative results are evident and that it is futile to expend more money in the future on the work.

Report Writing

Progress reports, as stated before, may be letter reports or whatever form the sponsor requires. Final reports or annual technical reports on the work may also have a particular format prescribed by the sponsor. This is especially true on Department of Defense or other government contracts. It is very important, from a contractual standpoint, to comply with the sponsor's wishes in regard to report content and format. Consequently, the following information should be used as a guide only for the structure of reports which are not specifically detailed in the contract for the work.

Final reports are the product of the research organization. Through the use of these reports the researcher acquaints the sponsor with the complete results of his work. The reports, therefore, are a vital link between the research organization and the potential user of the research results. In many cases, the researcher, who is most familiar with the work, does not have the inclination or the opportunity to carry his research into the application stage. Therefore, it is very important that he document his work in such a manner that it is useful to the potential developer or user of his results.

What can the researcher do to insure the preparation of a good report? One of the important aspects of a good report is its arrangement. In general a report should include the following:

1. Title
2. Author's name, organization, and mailing address
3. Table of contents
4. Nomenclature
5. Summary or abstract
6. Introduction
7. Description of experimental and theoretical work
8. Discussion of experimental and theoretical results
9. Conclusions
10. Recommendations

11. Suggested future programs
12. Appendices
      Bibliography, tables and illustrations, derivations, etc.

The title of a report should be explicit, descriptive, and as brief as possible while still conveying an adequate description of the work. A subtitle in parentheses may be added if necessary to clarify the meaning of the main title.

Many large research organizations have distinctive cover sheets for reports done on work under their cognizance. These cover sheets, to a large extent, will determine the format to be used in regard to the author's name, business address, and affiliation. If an organization does not have a distinctive cover for final reports, it should take steps to secure one. Examinations of reports of other reputable organizations will furnish ideas which may be used to create a design which, if used properly, will simplify format decision and, at the same time, standardize and characterize the product, the research report, of the research organization.

A table of contents is not always necessary. This is especially true if the report is brief and contains only a few pages. If, however, the report is broken down into the sections suggested and the report is fairly long, then it is important that the various sections be listed in a table of contents so that the interested reader will know where to look for a given section without paging through the whole report.

Some reports will not require a nomenclature. Often, however, reports for scientific research will contain many symbols which must be explained for the benefit of the reader. The symbols should be given, described grammatically, and their units precisely illustrated. A good nomenclature is vital to the understanding of highly technical reports. In some cases, it may be necessary to incorporate a glossary into the report to define terms whose meanings are not common knowledge. Such a glossary should be placed in the appendix.

The summary or abstract should contain a brief statement of the contents of the entire report. It should be able to stand alone and still have significant meaning. It should be so clear that the members of the organization to whom the report is submitted can obtain significant information from it alone. The summary or abstract is usually directed to the administrative officers of the sponsoring organization. These individuals do not have time to read a detailed report, and must get their information from cursory glances at technical reports and by briefings from their technical staff.

The introduction should accomplish, as indicated by its name, an introduction to the problem which was examined. It should include references of previous work and contain a historical background for the reader who is interested in details. The evolution of the trend of thought which culminated in the current research work should be given. Following the introduction to the project the actual experimental and theoretical work which was done on the project should be described. Because research reports are usually written for the technical man, they should be as concise as possible and not filled with unnecessary minute details. All terms, however, should be clearly defined. This is especially true if the work is to be read and interpreted by readers from different disciplines. For instance, transfer coefficients, conductivity, etc., should be specifically defined since they may have different units and meanings in various fields. No room for doubt should be left in regard to the definition of the various symbols used. It is permissible to refer to well-known experimental techniques, which have been well established by wide usage, and standard pieces of equipment by name or reference only. New methods or equipment should be described even if not original with the writer. One difficulty which is encountered in many reports is excessive utilization of references. If an author uses but does not discuss various references, he makes it difficult for the reader because the latter must go to a library and look them up in order to understand what is being stated. Sometimes it appears that writers utilize references to impress their readers, and, in some cases, references are used without having been read by the user. This, of course, can lead to embarrassment if some reader takes the trouble to check the references. In view of the above, it appears that a good technical report should stand on its own and not have to be propped up by the use of a large number of references which the report writer himself may not have read. Reports which are complete in themselves simplify things for the reader. He does not have to conduct an exhaustive literature search to see what was meant by various statements in the report. He will probably appreciate the thoroughness of the author.

If desired, pertinent tables of data and illustrations can be included as they are discussed in the report. In some cases, it may be feasible to place all of the tables and figures at the end of the report. This, however, will probably be dictated by sponsor requirements. The location of tables in the report structure may also be determined by their size. For instance, tables of only a few lines may be incorporated into the text, whereas tables containing a whole page of material may be assembled at the end of the report. Tables, of course, should have suitable descriptive headings and should be numbered consecutively. Graphs, charts, line drawings, etc., should also be properly identified with a figure number and descriptive title.

In the discussion of the results of the work, the information should be clear and concise. Reasons for the agreement or disagreement between theory and experiment should be explained. Each table and illustration should be discussed and its purpose in the project pointed out. This section should be written as clearly and objectively as possible so that the reader can follow the work from the text and illustrations and obtain a physical picture of the problem being examined. In the discussion of the experimental work, factual results should be pointed out and likely sources of discrepancies between anticipated and actual results should be explained, if possible. Overall conclusions should not be made in this section since they are reserved for later incorporation into the report; however, it is permissible to discuss the reasons for agreement or disagreement of the experimental data and the theoretical analyses.

In the conclusions section of the report the obvious results of the work are listed in accordance with their importance. The conclusions are stated briefly without discussion. The discussion should have been completed in the preceding sections of the report.

Recommendations are usually treated somewhat like conclusions. They should be brief and they should give the reader a complete and concise statement as to what is recommended. If future programs are suggested, these should be briefly discussed. In the report they should not take the form of a new proposal for a research program. Rather, they should indicate how to capitalize on the research effort just completed.

Usually a bibliography is given in the appendices. If references are few in number and scattered throughout the report, it is proper to insert them as footnotes on the pages on which they occur. However, when many references are cited it is better to collect them in a bibliography section in the order of their presentation. When a reference is cited, its number in the bibliography is usually placed in parentheses in the text.

In regard to tables and figures, it is important that common sense be used. One good method for determining what is acceptable, if sponsor instructions are lacking, is to utilize a previous report as a model. This is the most satisfactory method for the neophyte researcher to use in writing his first effort. If a good model is utilized, the researcher will have no difficulty in turning out an acceptable report.

After the report is written it must be reproduced. The various methods of reproducing technical information differ in cost, durability, reusability, and the quality of the finished product. Several systems are relatively inexpensive and produce very attractive and acceptable documents. The master pages for these processes can easily be typed on standard typewriters, errors can easily be corrected, and the final product can reproduce many hundreds of copies. In addition, the master copies may be stored for a long time and can be rerun if additional copies are desired. Figures and photographs can readily be transferred to master sheets and run with the standard sheets on which the text is typed. In general, the research organization should have a photographic and printing laboratory which will handle the reproduction of the reports written by the technical men. If, however, a new research organization is being formed, all of the various systems of reproducing printed material should be examined and the best one selected for the anticipated requirements.

Publication of Results in Journals

Technical reports are written to satisfy policy or contractual requirements. For instance, Department of Defense research contracts require that at the end of the project a technical final report be written in accordance with various specifications laid down by the sponsoring agency. These reports are usually detailed, complete, and contain all of the information generated in the course of the research. They, in the form submitted to the government, are usually not satisfactory for publication in technical journals of the various scientific and engineering societies. Therefore, it is necessary for the researcher to condense and rewrite the results of his research if he desires to submit them for publication in a technical journal.

One important reason for publishing in journals is that the chance of the research results being lost or poorly disseminated is decreased. Even though technical reports for the Department of Defense, NASA, AEC, and others are listed in ASTIA (Armed Services Technical Information Agency—now the Defense Documentation Center) and other summaries, the vast numbers of these reports make it almost certain that much of the work, if it is not immediately applicable, will fade into obscurity. This fact, together with the information explosion, has created a whole new science, that of information retrieval. Research is now being conducted to develop methods for the retrieval of specific information from the large, jumbled supply available, much of which is of questionable value. Many large research organizations have special sections whose only purpose is to search the literature for references on specified subjects. These literature searchers are valuable because they often turn up important pieces of work. In addition, they aid measurably in the preparation of bibliographies for proposals, reports, and technical papers.

Preparing a paper for a journal is different from preparing a technical report on a project. In technical journals space is usually at a premium; therefore, papers in excess of four thousand words are often too lengthy to be acceptable. The researcher must, therefore, be able to write another type of report, that for a technical journal. It is essential, however, for the researcher not to offer the results of his investigation for publication until he has received permission from the sponsor of the work as well as from his superior.

The Journal Article

The main purpose of a paper published in a technical journal is to convey information to technically trained personnel on new aspects of a given facet of the general area of interest covered by the journal. With the broad spectrum of interests that exist within each discipline, it is natural that many of the readers will be far less familiar with the specific subject of the paper than is the author. Therefore, the author should be very careful in defining his terms, and should use commonplace expressions to the maximum possible extent. If it is necessary to use highly technical phraseology, then it is desirable to repeat these phrases in simpler language. The author should at all times strive to write simply. If he does this, then it may be possible for him to create a paper which is intelligible to the average reader. Often a highly specialized researcher will have difficulty reaching a state of proper communion with the average engineer.

Papers should be written in the third person without mention of personal accomplishment. If it is necessary to use the first person in reference to various individuals, this should be done in such a manner as to minimize personal bias.

One big handicap for many researchers is their inability to spell words correctly. Of course, in many cases, this handicap stems from laziness. It is, however, very important that all the words in a paper, including unusual technical terms, be correctly spelled. Because the author's name will be associated with a published paper for posterity, it is apparent that he should make every effort to assure that it is as correct as possible.

As stated before, a journal paper should rarely exceed 4,000 words in length. This is approximately 14 pages of double-spaced typed manuscript. Figures and tables should be added to clarify the meaning of the results described. The old saying, *"A picture is worth 10,000 words,"* is applicable here.

It is important for the author, and is his responsibility, to secure publication approvals as may be contractually required. Work done on government contracts, if unclassified, can usually be published if a proper notation is incorporated into the paper giving the pertinent information as to which agency supported the work. The government contract may detail the steps necessary to publish the results of the research being supported by the contract. If not, the contracting officer will provide this information on request. Industrial sponsors, however, may desire to refrain from publishing research results. This is especially true if important proprietary information has been obtained. Classified government contracts also pose a special problem if publication is desired in journals. The results of these contracts are usually security classified and, therefore, cannot be published in the open literature. Fortunately, more and more classified conferences on particular subjects are being held where classified papers can be presented. It is becoming possible, therefore, for the researcher who works on a classified government contract to satisfy, at least partially, his desire to publish.

Contents of the Paper

Paper manuscripts are generally similar to technical reports in structure. A typical journal report will be prepared in accordance with the following pattern:

1. Title
2. Author's name and affiliation
3. Summary or abstract
4. Main contents of paper (such as: introduction, procedures, discussion of results, conclusions, etc.)
5. Appendices
6. Acknowledgements
7. Bibliography or references
8. Tables and figures, including graphs, charts, sketches, diagrams, etc.

In general, the title of the paper should be as explicit and descriptive as possible. In some cases it may be possible to use an explanatory subtitle to clarify the meaning. This, however, should be avoided if possible.

The author's name should appear immediately under the title and his business affiliation should be noted as a footnote on the bottom of the first page. This will permit the reader to place the author and his work in its proper perspective.

The summary or abstract of the paper should be placed on the first page under the author's name. Typically, it should contain approximately 100 words and indicate clearly the object and scope of the work. It should also outline, briefly, the most important results that were obtained. It should not detail or condense the whole paper. The primary purpose of the summary or abstract is to provide potential readers of the paper with the opportunity of quickly determining whether or not it is worthwhile for them to read the paper in detail. With the vast amount of literature being generated, it is self-evident that summaries are very important to the busy individual.

The main body of the paper should be organized into a logical sequence of sections which will permit the reader to follow the author's research program in an orderly manner. The main purpose of the research and the author's method of attack should be clearly stated in the opening pages of the paper. This should be followed by a short history of the problem, various means utilized for past solutions, and any other pertinent information to justify the method of approach that was used to conduct the investigation. A separate section describing details and results of the work then usually follows. It is important to close the paper by concisely summarizing the results of the work, including conclusions and any recommendations the author may have.

If the foregoing description of the body of the paper has left some readers with the conviction that a paper must conform to the example sequence of items given, this is not so. Some papers are written in an entirely different manner. In general, however, the items and contents, as illustrated, will result in an acceptable paper.

Some papers are highly theoretical and contain large amounts of detailed mathematics. It is sometimes advisable to put derivations of theoretical formulae in an appendix. This will make the paper much more readable and will still permit the reader who wants all the details to obtain them. Appendices can also be used for detailed descriptions of apparatus, procedures, and factors influencing the results where the incorporation of these facts in the main body of the paper would make the report uninteresting to the average reader.

The acknowledgements are usually placed at the end of the text, preceding the bibliography. In making the acknowledgements, contractual responsibility should be considered. It is wise for a research organization to set up some procedure for clearing all papers which are written for journal publication. This clearance, in some cases, is more than just a clearance for contractual obligations. Some large organizations require that the paper be reviewed by a committee to make sure that the research organization is not embarrassed by the submission of amateurish work. Figure 8–1 shows a typical form by which a large research organization monitors the papers of its staff. The form assures that the points discussed above are considered in the review of the paper. Figure 8–2 illustrates a routing sheet which goes with the paper as it is reviewed by an organizational committee who passes on the caliber of the work and decides whether or not the organization should be associated with the publication.

In general, tables which are less than five or six lines are included in the text. Proper captions should be placed over the table and they should be numbered consecutively. If the tables are extensive they should be

---

Date_____

MEMORANDUM TO: Secretary, Editorial Committee

FROM: (1)

SUBJECT: Request for editorial review of accompanying
                         manuscript.

(2) I am attaching hereto one copy of manuscript entitled:

(3) The authors are:_____

(4) It is intended for publication in:_____

(5) It reports, or pertains to, research done under project No._____

(6) The sponsor is_____

(7) The responsible Section is_____

(8) Before submitting the manuscript to the committee, the undersigned
    have given it a final review, and to the best of their knowledge it meets
    the following criteria:

	True	*False*
a. It is of sufficiently high quality to reflect professional credit on the company and authors	_____	_____
b. It does not violate security	_____	_____
c. It does not prematurely disclose patentable ideas.	_____	_____
d. It does not exceed contract limitations, especially any requirements that the results be kept confidential	_____	_____
e. It gives adequate acknowledgements to sponsors and other agencies	_____	_____
f. It conforms to the style and requirements of the journal to which it is being submitted	_____	_____

The Editorial Committee is requested to review the manuscript and return
to the undersigned as soon as possible

(9) Signed_____
                              Authors

(10) Signed_____
                             Supervisor

FIG. 8–1

Monitoring Form for Outside Publications

typed on separate sheets, properly labeled, and numbered in sequence.

In many cases photographs of experimental apparatus
or, in some cases, photographic data are included in a

EDITORIAL COMMITTEE ACTION RECORD   Date_____

Title:_____

Authors:_____

1. Division Director
   Comments:

   Date forwarded: Signed:

2. Committee Member
   Comments:

   Date forwarded: Signed:

3. Committee Chairman
   Comments:

   Date forwarded: Signed:

4. Recommendations:

5. Date returned to authors and supervisor with recommendations:____ __

FIG. 8–2

Editorial Action Record of Manuscript Review for
Outside Publications

report. Most reproduction schemes that are used require that a glossy photographic print be submitted for each photograph used. All photographs should be properly captioned with a figure number and title. In sending the report through the mail, care should be taken to assure that the photographs are not creased or marred in any way. The best way for mailing is to place the photographs between two flat pieces of cardboard. They should not be rolled or folded.

Graphs, charts, sketches, etc., should be drawn with black ink on heavy white paper. Blue prints, ozalids, photostatic prints, etc., are usually not suitable. Each figure should be properly numbered and captioned. Photographs and illustrations are usually sent to an engraver to be made into half-tones or line cuts, while the text goes to a printer to be set up in type. Therefore, it is advisable that each figure be properly identified by the author's name. This can be done by writing the name and title of the paper lightly on the back of the figure. In the case of photographs care should be taken to see that the marking does not penetrate the paper and mar the surface finish of the picture.

Writing the Paper

Some individuals can start from scratch and write a good paper, while others require some prior planning before the actual writing is begun.

The first step in any paper preparation is to have the experimental data and figures in a form which tells pictorially what was done. After this, it is comparatively easy for an author to make an outline, which embodies his ideas and thoughts into a logical sequence so that the actual transformation of these thoughts and ideas into written material is straightforward. By this technique, the author is actually writing his text around the figures and tables. Of course, in the process of making the outline, it may become necessary or desirable to rearrange figures and tables from the sequence of the original pictorial set-up. The use of a proper outlining procedure will do much to alleviate the dread many authors have of the task of writing. Potential authors should not even think about the actual writing until after the outline is prepared. If they can do away with the dread of writing they will accomplish much more in their productive careers.

Much can be said about the procedure for incorporating tables and figures into the text. The actual use of these illustrations is generally specified by the journal to which the paper is being submitted, and such instructions should be followed as carefully as possible. If this type of information is not available, an examination of current copies of the journal will readily indicate standard practices.

After the paper is written, the manuscript should be typed, double spaced, on one side of standard letter-size paper ($8\frac{1}{2}$ by 11 inches). Sufficient margins should be allowed on the edges for editing notations, etc. Four copies of the manuscript are usually required by the journal publisher. These copies are used to shorten the review time, since it is customary to distribute manuscripts to several reviewers at the same time. The extra copies can be carbon replicas of the original manuscript or some other acceptable reproductions.

After the reviewers' comments are received, the author is usually given the opportunity to incorporate them, if they will help the paper, into his manuscript. He then resubmits the manuscript for publication. Of course, in some cases, the manuscript is rejected by the journal. If this happens the author has two recourses: one, he can resubmit the article to another (perhaps less critical or more appropriate) publication; or two, he can re-evaluate his paper in the light of the criticisms of the reviewers and start all over again. The procedure for submitting papers for possible presentation at technical meetings is approximately the same as that just described.

Review of Papers for Publication

Many technical societies have instituted the review procedure to assure, in this time of very complex disciplines, that only papers of the highest quality are published or presented at their meetings. In the review process it is considered desirable for the intellectual process to be both objective and subjective. The reviewer is asked to be objective in the sense that he should try to eliminate any personal bias he may have towards the author or the topic under consideration. He is requested also to be subjective and evaluate the paper in the light of his own experience and knowledge of the field covered. It can readily be seen, therefore, that a paper which is well written and technically sound has little to fear from the review process. The poorly prepared paper should be, and usually is, rejected.

The editors and program chairman receive appreciable help from their reviewers. The review comments and informal appraisals by eminently qualified specialists are vital in this age of specialization. The comments are usually confidential and, in some sense, this is contrary to the democratic way of life, since one is judged without knowing the names of his accusers. Authors can do little about this and, therefore, must play the game of publications according to the current rules.

Summary

In this chapter the presentation of the results of the research effort has been discussed. Methods of presenting the results as well as the importance of writing good technical reports, even on disappointing research results, were considered. Report format, tone, and preparation procedure were detailed, and the publication of results in trade and technical journals was discussed. The discussions emphasized that the product of research effort is the technical report. This report is the intermediary between the original idea and the final product or application for which the work was originally started. It should be evident that if the original researcher were able to carry the results of his research through to the production stage, then a completely detailed technical report might not be necessary. However, even in this case, for historical reasons, it is preferable that the research results be documented properly in a technical report.

The research report serves many important purposes. It maintains good sponsor relations, it documents the effort for posterity, and it may permit a production man to utilize the results of the work to secure a useful product for mankind's benefit.

The publication of research results in technical journals also serves many useful purposes, and typical procedures for preparing the manuscript, submitting it for editorial review, and accomplishing associated details, were discussed. The discussion included typical examples of format and structure for journal articles; however, specific information on the custom and specifications followed by a particular journal should be obtained directly from the editors or by using a copy of the journal as a model.

Proper clearances from government or industrial sponsors should be obtained before the manuscript is submitted. This is the responsibility of the principal investigator on the research project.

Chapter 9

Utilizing
Research and Development
Results

THE APPLICATION of the research and development results is of the utmost importance. If the exploitation of the research results is inadequate, the research effort has been reduced to an academic exercise. Of course, when the program is initially of a basic or academic type, there may not be an economical reason to develop for production or utilize the results of the research. In most cases, however, research and development effort is aimed at increasing the economic advantage of the company or organization sponsoring the work. Therefore, it is important that the termination of the research and development effort be followed by an adequate program of evaluation which will assure maximum economical utilization of the results of the research effort; that is, research results must be put to work.

In some cases, a research program may be directed at the problem of determining whether or not the sponsoring company should enter a new field of production. The make-or-buy concept in this case predominates. If the make-or-buy problem was the reason for the research effort, it is vital that the results of the study provide sufficient information to make possible an unequivocal decision.

Research sponsored by the government may or may not have a product associated with it. Government sponsored research may be of a basic nature or of an applied nature to satisfy some specific requirement. Government sponsorship can sometimes be utilized by an industrial firm to form a base of support for a basic research staff. This does not mean, however, that the staff should forego looking for practical applications for their work. Consequently, even in basic research operations, in industry, a continuous effort should be maintained to search for opportunities to apply the research results to practical or profitable purposes.

One important item, which has not been mentioned heretofore, is the necessity of protecting the results of the research effort from exploitation by competitors. Two methods of protection may be utilized. The use of either or both methods depends on the type of product or process requiring protection. The first method involves patents and copyrights. Legal rights are granted by the various governments which issue the patents. The second method is one which requires secrecy. It is characterized by the name *trade secret*. The trade-secret type of protection is obtained by restricting information concerning recipes, process operation, etc. One prominent engineer in a conference mentioned that he would prefer not to patent a new production process, but would rather isolate the system and with a few trusted employees turn out the new product. By this means he could get a jump on his competitors and, at the same time, deny them the information required to compete with him in the market place. As an afterthought he mentioned that he obtained many of his good ideas from reading the patents of other companies. The trade-secret type of operation has led to much spying in industry. Industrial spies are paid extremely well for the information they possess. Industrial spying is utilized not only to spy out new products and processes, it is utilized to determine policy and economic decisions of top management which may have major influences on market conditions.

The more prevalent method of protecting new products and processes is through the use of patents and copyrights. Patents are utilized to protect the physical aspects of the research work while copyrights are utilized to protect the drawings, charts, etc., from unlicensed use by other organizations.

In general, after a new product or process has been invented or developed, it is important to do two things, namely: (1) determine the economic potential of the product or process; and (2) protect the end result of the research for the benefit of the sponsoring organization.

Protecting the Research and Development Result

After the research is completed, several basic questions must be answered before economic exploitation of the results is begun. One important question is whether or not a patent should be obtained. The fact that large sums of money have been expended in the research and development effort does not in itself provide the justification for filing a patent or, in some cases, a series of patents. Patent litigation and searches, are expensive and may not be warranted by the products of the research.

The first step in deciding whether or not a patent should be obtained is to make certain that the product is practical and has a market potential. Many researchers believe that their brainchild is unique and the answer to the world's problems. They also believe that their company or, in case they belong to a profit-sharing organization, themselves will profit immensely merely by patenting their ideas. This is where a major mistake is made. Profits cannot be accrued from a patent unless it covers a marketable or commercially advantageous item. It is, therefore, important that good market research analyses be made prior to spending large sums on expensive patent litigation.

An important step in the process of patenting the results of the research effort is the assembling of all the research records that have been kept on the project. These will provide proof of conception dates for the various ideas involved in the inventions. Written descriptions and drawings are excellent means of documenting ideas. All records should have been witnessed by one or more research associates. Witnessing signatures should be dated and it is important for the witnesses to understand the ideas and concepts under consideration. Correspondence, sales slips for materials, drawings, sketches, diaries, memos, and models should be kept on hand in case they are needed to prove the facts and dates of the various phases of the inventive procedure.

Many large organizations have standard record-of-invention forms which should be filled out and properly witnessed. Figures 9–1 and 9–2 are representative of forms utilized for this purpose. It is also standard practice for well-managed research organizations to issue project notebooks to the project director and his staff. It is usually required that these notebooks be kept up-to-date and that important entries be dated and witnessed, since it is possible that these may have important bearing on patent litigation in the future.

When a product appears to be economically useful, then it is important to make a search of the patent literature in order to determine whether or not the proposed invention is original. The initial patent search is relatively inexpensive and will determine the advisability of proceeding with a patent application. It is sometimes evident from the patent search that parts of the proposed invention have already been anticipated in prior art; however, it may also indicate that certain parts of the invention are new and therefore worthwhile. In this case, it may be wise to attempt to obtain patent protection on only part of the original idea. The patent search may also reveal other inventions which are better than the one proposed. In this case, money will be saved by abandoning the project.

A patent search is made in the Search Room of the Patent Office in Washington, D.C. Many patent attorneys have offices or associate arrangements with lawyers in Washington, D.C., so that they can easily arrange for patent searches to be made. Large companies maintain their own patent attorneys and, consequently, are relatively skilled in patent matters. For the organizations or individuals who do not possess ready access to patent attorneys, the Patent Office will provide a list of practicing patent practitioners in specified geographic areas. Requests for this list should be addressed to the Commissioner of Patents, Patent Office, U.S. Department of Commerce, Washington, D.C. All correspondence with patent attorneys should be retained since it provides proof of an intention to patent and also affords protection against unethical exploitation.

INSTRUCTIONS FOR PREPARATION OF RECORD OF INVENTION

A Record of Invention is a very important legal document, and proper care in its early and complete preparation will save much time and inconvenience in the future should the invention ever become involved in a controversy. If necessary, obtain the help of the technical information service of the SEES. Separate Record of Invention forms must be prepared for each distinct invention. This Record of Invention form was prepared to fit all possible conditions and therefore contains questions which may not be applicable to certain inventors. If a question cannot be answered, mark it "does not apply," "no" or "none," etc.

1. Give name in full—JOHN ALLEN DOE or JOHN A. DOE, and position. J. ALLEN DOE will not be accepted by the Patent Office.

2. Give complete details—name, address, phone and extension, city, state.

3. Indicate date first employed.

4. Give your present address. This is your residence address.

5. If No. 4 is a temporary address, give a permanent address where mail can be sent and forwarded regardless of your temporary location. If No. 4 is your permanent address, No. 5 may be marked "Same as No. 4."

6. The question as to whether an invention was actually conceived by one person or by the cooperation of several persons is vitally important to the validity of the patent. Incorrect decisions of sole or joint inventorship will result in an *invalid patent*. Personal feelings and friendships must not influence the answer to this question. To merely present a problem does not make one an inventor. He must contribute to the solution of the problem to be classed as an inventor. A mechanic who builds a device under the supervision of an inventor is not a joint inventor. If there is any doubt, obtain assistance.

7. A short title briefly describing the invention. For instance, "Method and Apparatus for Preparing Segmental Carbon Rings," "Uni-directional Antenna," or "Packing Gland Wrench."

8. A list is desired of all pertinent material which forms the "Disclosure of Invention," thereby relating the Record of Invention to the disclosure. Give accurate print reference numbers, photo numbers, etc., identifying sketches by date and/or some other reference.

9. This is the date on which the general "idea" was "born". State briefly circumstances relative to conception. For example, on 2 February 1945, I saw accident to John A. Doe while working on circular saw and need for a guard was apparent. Immediately made sketch for a suitable guard and presented it to James Smith, my foreman. Or, test for signal generator was unsuccessful for several months. On 21 January 1946 made change in circuit by changing capacity and location of by-pass condenser and installing suitable chokes.

10. This date may coincide with No. 9, will never be earlier, but may be later.

11. This date also may be the same as No. 9 and No. 10, or different from either one, but never earlier than No. 9.

12. The disclosure of the invention may be by orally telling someone of your invention, by showing and explaining descriptions and drawings, or by demonstrating the operation of a model or full scale device. The person(s) to whom an invention is disclosed may make an excellent witness if the invention is ever involved in a controversy and it is to the inventor's advantage to see that his invention is understood. It is preferable to ask the witness to read and sign the description and drawings, using the statement "Disclosed to and understood by my this _____ day of _____ 19__" Notebook entries should be handled in a like manner. Indicate persons' position, connection with outside commercial firm, or other pertinent information. State if orally, by sketch or other form.

13. If no model or full scale device was made, so state. Answers to Nos. 14 to 18 inclusive should be marked "does not apply."

14. Indicate where model or full scale device may be seen in the event the attorney desires to witness its operation.

FIG. 9–1

RECORD OF INVENTION FORM AND INSTRUCTION PART I

15. State whether first tests were successful or unsuccessful and briefly outline results.

16. Witnesses to tests are important. Identify them so they can be located later if necessary.

17. Tell briefly results of later tests, and give data on witnesses.

18. It is desirable to record carefully the results of all tests and to preserve such records. A copy of these test results may form a part of the invention disclosure to assist the attorney in preparing the case.

19. In related inventions, much repetition can be avoided by reference to the previous invention(s), if any. Identify such records or reports by title, inventor, date, number, etc.

20. Most inventions are improvements over existing devices. References to the devices which have been improved are very helpful to the attorney preparing the patent application. Such references may consist of patent numbers, issued patents, pending applications, articles published in technical magazines, listing in catalogs or trade journals, or any other published record of the invention.

21. The law provides that after an invention has been in "Public Use" for more than one year it becomes public property and cannot be protected by Letters Patent. The question of public use is a debatable one. The same is true of experimental use, and it is sometimes difficult to ascertain when experimental use ceases and public use begins. A statement as to the use of your invention with sufficient details as to the circumstances will assist in determining whether public use exists. Differentiate, if possible, between use by the Government and commercial use.

22. Where details of the invention have been released to a firm or activity, it is important to record the data to clearly fix the facts of the release of information. The firm may be under contract with a federal agency. If so, the contract number should be given.

23. If classified, the proper classification is to be stamped on both the top and bottom of each page.

FIG. 9–1 (Cont.)

RECORD OF INVENTION FORM AND INSTRUCTION PART I

RECORD OF INVENTION—Part I

This is an important legal document. Read instructions carefully before filling in data.
Prepare in Quadruplicate

PROJECT NO. _____

CONTRACT NO. _____   RECOMMENDED SECURITY   REC. OF
                         CLASSIFICATION _____   INV. NO. _____

1. NAME OF INVENTOR	POSITION

2. DEPARTMENT OR DIVISION

3. DATES OF EMPLOYMENT

4. PRESENT ADDRESS (No. Street, City, County, State)	TELEPHONE	PERMANENT OR UNTIL

5. PERMANENT ADDRESS (No. Street, City, County, State)	TELEPHONE

6. NAME(S) AND ADDRESS(ES) OF CO-INVENTORS (if any)

7. DESCRIPTIVE TITLE OF INVENTION

8. LIST DRAWINGS, SKETCHES, PHOTOS, REPORTS, DESCRIPTIONS, NOTEBOOK ENTRIES, ETC. WHICH SHOW OR DESCRIBE INVENTION

9. EARLIEST DATA AND PLACE INVENTION WAS CONCEIVED (Brief outline of circumstances)

10. DATE AND PLACE OF FIRST SKETCH, DRAWING OR PHOTO

11. DATE AND PLACE OF FIRST WRITTEN DESCRIPTION

12.   **DISCLOSURE OF INVENTION TO OTHERS**

NAME, TITLE AND ADDRESS	FORM OF DISCLOSURE	DATE AND PLACE OF DISCLOSURE	WAS SIGNATURE OBTAINED (YES OR NO)

12A. IMPORTANT—HAVE ANY PUBLICATIONS OR REPORTS BEEN MADE ON THIS INVENTION?

13. DATE AND PLACE OF COMPLETION OF FIRST OPERATING MODEL OR FULL SIZE DEVICE

14. PRESENT LOCATION OF MODEL

15. DATE, PLACE, DESCRIPTION AND RESULTS OF FIRST TEST OR OPERATION

FIG. 9–1 (Cont.)

RECORD OF INVENTION FORM AND INSTRUCTION PART I

16. NAMES AND ADDRESSES OF WITNESSES OF FIRST TEST

17. DATE, PLACE, DESCRIPTION AND RESULTS OF LATER TESTS (name witnesses)

18. IDENTIFY RECORDS OF TESTS AND GIVE PRESENT LOCATION OF RECORDS

19. PRIOR REPORTS OR RECORDS OF INVENTION TO WHICH INVENTION IS RELATED

20.   **OTHER KNOWN CLOSELY RELATED PATENTS, PATENT APPLICATIONS AND PUBLICATIONS**

PATENT OR APPLICATION NO.	DATE	TITLE OF INVENTION OR PUBLISHED ARTICLE	NAME OF PUBLICATION

21. EXTENT OF USE: PAST, PRESENT AND CONTEMPLATED (Give dates, places and other pertinent details)

22.   **DETAILS OF INVENTION HAVE BEEN RELEASED TO THE FOLLOWING COMPANIES OR ACTIVITIES**

NAME AND ADDRESS	INDIVIDUAL OR REPRESENTATIVE	CONTRACT NO.	DATE

SIGNATURE OF INVENTOR   DATE

FIG. 9–1 (Cont.)

RECORD OF INVENTION FORM AND INSTRUCTION PART I

RECORD OF INVENTION—Part II

(Attach to Record of Invention Part I)

REC. OF
INV. NO. _____

The Disclosure of Invention should be written up in the inventor's own words and generally should follow the outline given below. Sketches, prints, photos and other illustrations as well as reports of any nature in which the invention is referred to, if available, should form a part of this disclosure and reference can be made thereto in the description of construction and operation.

1. INVENTORS NAME(S)

2. TITLE OF INVENTION

For answers to following questions use remainder of sheet, other side, and attach extra sheets if necessary.

3. GENERAL PURPOSE OF INVENTION. STATE IN GENERAL TERMS THE OBJECTS OF THE INVENTION.

4. DESCRIBE OLD METHOD(S), IF ANY, OF PERFORMING THE FUNCTION OF THE INVENTION.

5. INDICATE THE DISADVANTAGES OF THE OLD MEANS OR DEVICE(S).

6. DESCRIBE THE CONSTRUCTION OF YOUR INVENTION, SHOWING THE CHANGES, ADDITIONS AND IMPROVEMENTS OVER THE OLD MEANS OR DEVICES

7. GIVE DETAILS OF THE OPERATION IF NOT ALREADY DESCRIBED UNDER 6.

8. STATE THE ADVANTAGES OF YOUR INVENTION OVER WHAT HAS BEEN DONE BEFORE.

9. INDICATE ANY ALTERNATE METHODS OF CONSTRUCTION.

10. IF A JOINT INVENTION, INDICATE WHAT CONTRIBUTION WAS MADE BY EACH INVENTOR.

11. FEATURES WHICH ARE BELIEVED TO BE NEW.

12. AFTER THE DISCLOSURE IS PREPARED, IT SHOULD BE SIGNED BY THE INVENTOR(S), AND THEN READ AND SIGNED AT THE BOTTOM OF EACH PAGE BY TWO WITNESSES USING THE FOLLOWING STATEMENT:
"DISCLOSED TO AND UNDERSTOOD BY ME THIS_____DAY OF_____19__

SIGNATURE_____ "

FIG. 9–2
RECORD OF INVENTION FORM PART II

RECORD OF INVENTION—Part II

SKETCHES (if required)

INSTRUCTIONS:

1. PREPARE ON OZALID MASTER OR TISSUE, USING ADDITIONAL PAGES IF REQUIRED.
2. NUMBER OR LETTER EACH SKETCH.

SIGNATURE OF INVENTOR_____DATE_____

DISCLOSED TO AND UNDERSTOOD BY US THIS_____DAY

OF_____19_____

_____

WITNESS

_____

WITNESS

FIG. 9–2 (Cont.)
RECORD OF INVENTION FORM PART II

After the search has been completed, it is necessary to determine the exact extent of coverage that can be obtained on the original ideas or inventions. This is the final phase of the determination as to whether or not it is desirable to file patent applications. Here the advice of good patent attorneys is very valuable. They, with their background of experience in patent matters, will probably be able to guide the inventors in making an intelligent decision in this matter. The actual preparation of the patents should be done by those experienced with the rigid requirements pertaining to drawings, descriptions, etc., which are specified by the Patent Office. The patent laws require that the patent specification provide an adequate description of the invention. This description should be sufficiently clear that a person skilled in the field of applicability of the patented item can make and use it. The patent must also contain definite statements or claims which describe the uniqueness of the invention and which distinguish it from other patents already in force. The number of important claims obtained may, to a large extent, determine the commercial value of the patent. It is wise not to limit the patent by being too modest with the claims.

Marketing the Research Results

Although it is not the purpose of this discussion to provide a guide for marketing research results, it is important that the philosophy associated with this topic be understood by researchers and research managers. The comment has been made time and time again that management must understand the nature and objectives of research and researchers. Conversely, it is important that the researcher understand the objectives of management. Management must make a profit to stay in business and supply the facilities and livelihood of the researchers. Therefore, it is important that the overall results of research assist the managers in their goal of creating a profit for the organization.

After the patent has been applied for and essentially secured, the marketing procedure is free to take place. The economic potential of a patent can be realized by several means. These are:

1. Manufacture the item and sell it;
2. License other manufacturers to make the product and obtain royalties from their efforts; and,
3. Manufacture and license the product.

Large production organizations usually will choose to manufacture a new product or employ a new process themselves if it is within the scope of their projected product plan. However, it may be unrealistic to engage in competitive manufacture, particularly if the new product does not fit readily into the company product line. In such a case, the new product can be licensed to organizations which have a market and the necessary sales and advertising personnel to promote the product. Thus licensing is a means of obtaining economic benefits without the expenditure of large sums of money.

Occasionally a new product or process may have a future value for the company which is more attractive than its current value. In this case, the patent may be used to protect a current product from competition while an investment in production facilities is amortized.

Even though an idea is not readily applicable to the company's current product line, it may be valuable for the production of items not yet contemplated. By patenting all worthwhile and promising ideas, a progressive company protects itself against competition at later dates.

Obviously, the holder of a vital patent gains an appreciable strategic advantage in the market place. Hence, protective patenting is important for the future security of the company's market.

If a company decides to manufacture and sell an item it has patented, several procedures are available. These procedures include:

1. Manufacturing the item in company owned plants and selling it through a company distribution system;
2. Manufacturing the item in company owned plants and selling it through externally owned distribution systems;
3. Subcontracting the manufacture of the item to externally owned production plants and marketing it through a company owned distribution system; and,
4. Subcontracting the manufacture of the item to externally owned production plants and marketing it through externally owned distribution systems.

The above procedures are shown schematically in Figure 9–3. Company management can maintain control over the product by direct and indirect means. If the production and distribution are carried out in company owned organizations, the control is direct. If the production is in a company owned plant and the distribution is by an externally owned organization or its converse, then the control is partially direct and partially indirect. However, if both the production and distribution take place through externally owned organizations, then the control is completely indirect. The method to be utilized to determine how the product should be produced and marketed depends upon many factors. Typical factors involved are:

1. Cost of manufacture;
2. Cost of distribution;

3. Potential market location; and,

4. Established reputation in related product lines.

The cost of manufacturing a new product is very important in determining the course management should take in placing an item on the market. Surveys of

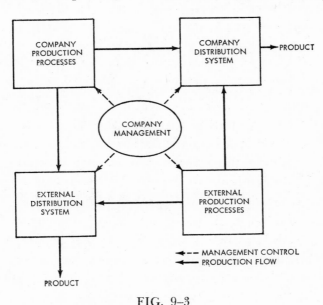

FIG. 9–3

MANUFACTURING AND MARKETING PROCESSES

the company's production facilities may indicate that the new product cannot be economically produced without an exorbitant investment in new production machinery and personnel. A subsequent investigation of the production capabilities of other manufacturers may indicate they are able to build the item, because of the availability of equipment and experience, at a much lower unit cost than would be possible by the use of internal company facilities. At this juncture, management must evaluate the relative merits of farming out the production as compared to building up an internal capability. Part of this evaluation is the recognition of the inherent danger in being too dependent on external sources of supply or service: it is not uncommon for an external producer to become a competitor if an opportunity—e.g. if the patent protection runs out—offers itself. In a final analysis, however, the economics of the situation may be such that the attractiveness of external production cannot be overlooked.

The cost of distribution of a new product is also a very important item to consider. If the item can be marketed more easily and at a lower cost through an external organization, then this approach should be employed. The considerations here are similar to those encountered in determining the relative cost of manufacturing the item. They can have an appreciable effect on the product's selling price and, consequently, on the profits.

Potential market location in relation to company facilities and distribution systems is very important. If the product is to be sold in an area remote from the company's sources of raw materials and production, then it will probably be advantageous to have the product manufactured by a production facility in the market location. This saves transportation costs which can become an appreciable percentage of the product's selling price. Secondary factors, such as availability and cost of labor, climate conditions, taxation, and available power sources, also enter into the decision of whether to manufacture the product using company facilities or external facilities. In the final review, an economic determination will probably govern the decision. Therefore, all factors which have an economic bearing on the problem must be included in the analysis.

Another item which must be considered concerns the reputation of the potential producer in related product fields. For example, a company which has an established reputation as a manufacturer of home appliances may have difficulty convincing the consumers that they are experts in pharmaceuticals. Hence, if the company un-covers a new, important drug it may be advantageous to market the item through a reputable drug manufactur-ing company, or distributor.

In the foregoing, the various ways of manufacturing and distributing a product have been discussed. It was mentioned previously that royalties from the licensing of new products and processes are one of the potential rewards of research and development. Therefore, it is important to consider how licensing enters into the economic picture. Royalties are cash returns resulting from permitting an external production organization to manufacture or use an item which is protected by pat-ents. They can be a lucrative source of funds to supple-ment a company's income, and are tangible evidence of the worth of the research effort and its associated support-ing activities.

Market development by more than one manufacturer is often accomplished by the licensing procedure. If production and licensing are jointly undertaken then the growth of a market may be accelerated. Figure 9–4 illustrates this phenomenon. By incorporating a licensee into the picture, additional production and promotional pressures can be applied to develop a potential market for the benefit of both the licensee and the licensor. Licensing also permits the exploitation of a patented item without creating an image of a monopolistic opera-tion.

If an organizational decision is made to build a facility for the production of an item which has been evolved through research and development efforts, a complicated and tedious program of activity usually must take place before production can begin. The phases involved in bringing a production system into operation are: organizational; engineering; construction; programming prior to start-up; and start-up and production.

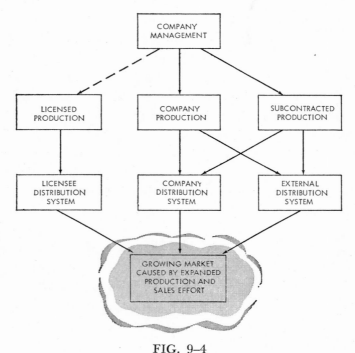

FIG. 9–4

EXPANDING A MARKET THROUGH LICENSEE PARTICIPATION

The organizational phase of any project involves planning, scheduling, and personnel recruiting effort. To obtain a good organizational structure it is necessary that a good project manager be selected. He will become the keystone of the entire production structure. This selection may be from within the company or from external sources depending upon the availability of personnel. It is not uncommon for this man to assume the responsibility of plant manager for the production facility after it is completed. Usually, project managers are selected from the ranks of the outstanding production engineers in the parent company.

In many cases the engineering phase of the program is accomplished with the help of outside engineering firms whose business it is to furnish engineering designs, analyses, reviews, and equipment specifications. These firms may even take over the construction and programming prior to start-up phases of the program. Many firms with excellent reputations are available to perform these technical services and their experience is very important to inexperienced companies.

Operations prior to start-up include bringing in and training the production personnel who will actually be responsible for the production operation of the plant and, consequently, for making a profit for the parent company. This is an extremely important phase of the production operation and one in which many companies have little experience. The success of the initial production operation may well depend upon the training program which has many facets including development of operating manuals, personnel selection, and personnel orientation. In some instances, the parent company may elect to contract for all of the pre-production services required. Then the organization, engineering, construction, personnel training, and start-up are all handled through external contractors. The selection and hiring of key personnel may be left to the parent company.

During the pre-production, as well as the production phases of an operation, it is important that close liaison be maintained with the research and development staff. The interrelations between research, development, and production were pointed out in Chapter 1. The organizational structure of the new operation should be established so that continual product and plant improvements will be possible. It is not uncommon to find that a project manager may try to delay production in order to incorporate new developments into his program. Top management must prevent undue delays in production since they may be economically detrimental. They may even cause a company to experience failure.

The proper utilization of production together with research and development does much to assure the economic success of an organization. It is, therefore, very important that these items be properly balanced. Too much research and not enough production can lead to procrastination and failure. Conversely, too much production and too little research will lead to a product which will become economically obsolete. The test of top management is its ability to maintain a proper balance between production and research.

Using Research Results to Generate New R and D Projects

Some organizations are not oriented towards product production, but are primarily set up to do research and development work. In order for such organizations to continue in business, it is necessary for them to continually create new ideas for research and development programs. This requires a creative staff. One of the best ways for a researcher to get ideas is to continually do research. Research operations, therefore, breed new research ideas. Consequently, research can be parlayed into more research. The exponential growth of the research operations in the United States indicates that this chain-reaction process is currently going on at a very rapid rate.

Basic research probably provides the best source for new ideas for more research. A chain-reaction effect, as indicated in Figure 1–2, illustrates the importance of basic research results. Applied research provides new ideas to a somewhat lesser degree. As a result, a progressive R and D organization will maintain a sufficient number of basic projects to assure that the chain reaction of ideas will be sustained, even though applied and development efforts are more lucrative.

Support for basic research may be difficult to obtain from industrial firms. Consequently, it is important to consider government support for such effort. In obtaining government support, proposals should be written in such a manner that they give free rein to the researcher to explore promising avenues which may open up in the course of the designated work. This will permit the parent organization to maintain a continuity of effort by writing successive proposals on new facets of the project as they arise. It seems paradoxical that a proposal should provide both broad and limited objectives at the same time. Experience in writing proposals allows this to be readily done, and one basic project, resulting from such a proposal, may generate many applied research and developmental efforts.

Summary

The economic benefits of research are important. They will not, however, be realized without proper utilization and exploitation of the research results. Consequently, the production and marketing of the products of the research effort are of prime importance.

When a marketable item has been obtained, the company must first protect the item from exploitation by others. This may be done by two main methods. First, patents should be obtained to provide legal rights to the item. Second, if the marketable item is made by a process or method which can be kept a secret, a trade-secret system of control may be feasible to protect the company's economic investment in the research. Trade secrets have led to industrial spying and, consequently, may not afford much protection from a persistent and sophisticated competitor.

Before a new product can be made into an economic asset, the problems of production and marketing must be met. Questions in regard to licensing, farming out production, establishing sales forces, etc., all enter into the problem. The four alternative procedures for the manufacture and sale of an item are manufacture and sale by company owned organizations; manufacture by the company, sale through outside distributorships; manufacture by outside organizations and sale through company channels; and finally, manufacture and sale by outside organizations. If this last system is decided upon, it may be better to license the item to another organization and collect royalties on the production. These royalties can become a lucrative source of funds to supplement a company's income. This procedure, however, is not recommended if the product is in the company's projected product lines. It may be feasible, in order to stimulate a market, to license and at the same time produce the product in company owned plants. By incorporating a licensee into the picture, additional production and promotional pressures can be applied to develop a potential market for the benefit of all.

Internal production of a new item can involve a complicated and tedious program to bring a new production facility into operation. This may require financing, hiring and training of men, and the building of new facilities. Experienced engineering firms are available to assist with these matters.

The continuation of organizations who primarily do research is dependent upon a continuous flow of new ideas for research projects. One of the best ways for a researcher to get new ideas is to do research. Consequently, it is desirable for purely research organizations to obtain government support for basic research programs in order for them to secure the chain-reaction of ideas necessary for their survival.

Chapter 1—References

ALLISON, DAVID. "The Civilian Technology Lag," *International Science and Technology* (December, 1963), pp. 24–34.

CAMPBELL, N. R. *What is Science?* New York: Dover Publications, 1952.

"Expenditures," *Industrial Research* (January, 1964), pp. 36–39.

FREEMAN, PAUL. *The Principles of Scientific Research.* London: MacDonald and Co., 1949.

HOLLOMON, J. HERBERT. "Technical Resources—Neglected by Industry?" *Mechanical Engineering*, Vol. 86, No. 1 (January, 1964), pp. 30–32.

KENYON, RICHARD L. "Support Versus Seduction of Basic Research Talent," *Chemical & Engineering News* (June 12, 1961), p. 7.

LUM, J. H. "Industry's Stake in Fundamental Research," *Industrial and Engineering Chemistry*, Vol. 49, No. 5 (1957), pp. 87A–92A.

MORGEN, R. A. "The Place of the National Science Foundation in the Basic Research Program," *Proceedings of the Sixth Annual Conference on the Administration of Research*, pp. 48–52. Atlanta: Georgia Institute of Technology, 1953.

NATIONAL SCIENCE FOUNDATION. *Federal Funds for Research, Development, and Other Scientific Activities* (formerly *Federal Funds for Science*), Fiscal Years 1962, 1963, and 1964, Vol. XII, Report No. 64–11.

——— *Funds for Research and Development in Industry 1958.* Report No. 61–32. Washington, D.C.: U.S. Government Printing Office, 1961.

——— *Investing in Scientific Progress 1961–1970.* Report No. 61–27. Washington, D.C.: U.S. Government Printing Office, 1961.

——— *Research and Development in Industry 1961.* Report No. 64–9. Washington, D.C.: U.S. Government Printing Office, 1964.

NATIONAL SCIENCE FOUNDATION. *Reviews of Data on Research and Development,* "Research and Development in the Aircraft and Missile Industry (1956–1961)," Report No. 39, 63–19, Washington, D.C.: U.S. Government Printing Office, May, 1963.

———— *Scientific and Technical Personnel in Industry.* Report No. 61–75. Washington, D.C.: U.S. Government Printing Office, 1960.

———— *Scientists and Engineers in the Federal Government.* Report No. 61–43. Washington, D.C.: U.S. Government Printing Office, October, 1958.

"Researching the Research Dollar," *Chemical Engineering Progress,* Vol. 57, No. 4 (April, 1961), p. 33.

U.S. BUREAU OF THE CENSUS. *Our Growing Population.* Graphic Pamphlets, GP 60–1, Washington, D.C.: U.S. Government Printing Office, 1961.

"U.S. Invests in Ideas—$13.5 Billion," *News Front* (September, 1961), pp. 10–17.

WILSON, E. B., JR. *An Introduction to Scientific Research.* New York: McGraw-Hill Book Co., 1952.

WORK, H. K. "A Research Engineer's View of Basic Research," *Proceedings of the Sixth Annual Conference on the Administration of Research,* pp. 41–45. Atlanta: Georgia Institute of Technology, 1953.

Chapter 2—References

"Administration in Education," *Science,* American Association for the Advancement of Science, Vol. 134, No. 3474 (July 28, 1961).

ALLISON, DAVID. "The Science Entrepreneur," *International Science and Technology* (January, 1963), pp. 40–45.

DANILOV, VICTOR J. "Build It Here," *Industrial Research* (May, 1963), pp. 17–22.

———— "Trends in University Research," *Industrial Research* (April, 1964), pp. 30–37.

FURNAS, C. C. "Organizing Complexity," *Mechanical Engineering,* Vol. 85, No. 7 (July, 1963), pp. 22–25.

GAUDET, F. J. "Manpower Wastage," *Mechanical Engineering,* Vol. 85, No. 7 (July, 1963) , pp. 38–39.

HALLIGAN, C. W. "The Role of 'Government' Nonprofit Research Corporations," *Industrial Research* (July–August, 1963) , pp. 32–39.

MANDELL, M. "Can You Afford Government Research and Development Contracts," *Industrial Research* (November, 1961) , pp. 13–19.

"NASA-Industry Program Plans Conference," George C. Marshall Space Flight Center, September 27–28, 1960.

"New Centers of Excellence," *Industrial Research* (May, 1964) , p. 7.

PELZ, DONALD C. "Freedom in Research," *International Science and Technology* (February, 1964) , pp. 54–66.

SEBRELL, W. H. JR. "Effects of Age, Size and Growth on the Vitality of Research Laboratories," *Proceedings of the Sixth Annual Conference on the Administration of Research,* pp. 24–30. Atlanta: Georgia Institute of Technology, 1953.

Sponsored Research Policy of Colleges and Universities. A Report of the Committee on Institutional Research Policy. Washington, D.C.: American Council on Education, 1954.

"University Research Report," *Industrial Research* (April, 1963) .

WHEADON, WILLIAM C. "Organizing University Research," *Industrial Research* (April, 1964) , pp. 38–47.

Chapter 3—References

ALLISON, DAVID. "The Affluent Consultants," *International Science and Technology* (October, 1962) , pp. 50–54.

——— "Educating the Engineer," *International Science and Technology* (June, 1963) , pp. 26–38.

——— "Engineer Renewal," *International Science and Technology* (June, 1964) , pp. 48–54.

APPLEY, L. A. "The Professional Manager," *Mechanical Engineering,* Vol. 86, No. 3 (March, 1964) , pp. 38–39.

BEST, ROBERT D. "The Scientific Mind Vs. the Management Mind," *Industrial Research* (October, 1963), pp. 50–52.

"Creativity," *Carnegie Corporation of New York Quarterly,* Vol. 9, No. 3 (July, 1961).

CURTIS, ROGER W. "International Conferences," *International Science and Technology* (November, 1962), pp. 38–41.

DANILOV, VICTOR J. "Technical Recruitment," *Industrial Research* (July–August, 1963), pp. 22–25.

FARRINGTON, WILLIAM. "Squeezing Research Dollars," *International Science and Technology* (September, 1963), pp. 77–83.

GORDON, W. J. J. "Director of Research," *The New Yorker* (November 4, 1961), pp. 48–52.

INGERSOLL, A. C. "Educating Tomorrow's Engineers," *Mechanical Engineering,* Vol. 85, No. 12 (December, 1963), pp. 20–21.

LEVIN, BEATRICE. "Winning the Wives," *Industrial Research* (July–August, 1963), pp. 18–19.

NATIONAL SCIENCE FOUNDATION. *Investing in Scientific Progress 1961–1970.* Report No. 61–27. Washington, D.C.: U.S. Government Printing Office, 1961.

―――― *Research and Development in Industry 1961.* Report No. 64–9. Washington, D.C.: U.S. Government Printing Office, 1964.

―――― *Scientific and Technical Personnel in American Industry.* Report on a 1959 Survey, No. 60–62. Washington, D.C.: U.S. Government Printing Office, 1960.

―――― *Scientific and Technical Personnel in Industry.* Report No. 61–75. Washington, D.C.: U.S. Government Printing Office, 1960.

―――― *Scientists and Engineers in the Federal Government.* Report No. 61–43. Washington, D.C.: U.S. Government Printing Office, October, 1958.

Research Conference on the Identification of Creative Scientific Talent—1959. (Also 1955 and 1957.) Salt Lake City: University of Utah Press, 1959.

(Extensive bibliography on creativity, requirements for research personnel, etc.)

Research is People. New York: Industrial Research Institute, Inc., and New York University Press, 1956.

SMITH, R. B. "Keeping Pace with the Scientific Age?" *Mechanical Engineering,* Vol. 85, No. 10 (October, 1963), pp. 26–27.

TORPEY, W. G. "The Obsolescent Engineer," *Mechanical Engineering,* Vol. 85, No. 10 (October, 1963), pp. 28–29.

U.S. BUREAU OF THE CENSUS. *Statistical Abstract of the United States: 1965,* 86th ed. Washington, D.C.: U.S. Government Printing Office, 1965.

Chapter 4—References

ACKOFF, R. L. *Scientific Method: Optimizing Applied Research Decision.* New York: John Wiley and Sons, Inc., 1962.

BATES, A. G. "Executive Decisions in the Chemical Lab," *Industrial and Engineering Chemistry* Vol. 51, No. 5 (1959), pp. 97A–102A.

BAUMOL, W. J. *Business Behavior, Value and Growth.* New York: The Macmillan Co., 1959.

——— *Economic Theory and Operations Analysis.* Englewood Cliffs, N.J. Prentice-Hall, Inc., 1961.

BEACH, E. F. *Economic Models.* New York: John Wiley and Sons, 1957.

BROWN, RALPH. "Vitality of a Research Institution and How to Maintain It," *Proceedings of the Sixth Annual Conference on the Administration of Research,* pp. 31–35. Atlanta: Georgia Institute of Technology, 1953.

COLLIER, D. W. "R & D—Government or Industry," *Mechanical Engineering,* Vol. 85, No. 10 (October, 1963), pp. 30–32.

FARRIS, HANSFORD W. "The Campus and Industry," *Industrial Research* (April, 1964), pp. 76–81.

HAPPEL, JOHN. *Chemical Process Economics.* New York: John Wiley and Sons, Inc., 1958.

HUTCHESON, JOHN. "Organizing Research," *International Science and Technology* (November, 1962), pp. 66–70.

LINCOLN, PHILIP A. "The Data Deluge," *Industrial Research* (September, 1963), pp. 18–19.

LITTAUER, S. B. "Technological Stability in Industrial Operations," *Transactions of the New York Academy of Science,* Ser. II, 13, No. 2, 1950, pp. 66–72.

MACDONALD, B. I., AND FRANKS, W. S. "Economic and Business Factors in Piloting Specialty Chemicals," *Chemical Engineering Progress,* Vol. 58 (February, 1962), pp. 67–69.

MILLER, D. W. AND STARR, M. K. *Executive Decisions and Operations Research.* Englewood Cliffs, N.J.: Prentice-Hall, Inc., 1960.

RIPPERGER, E. A., WOOSTER, H. AND JUHASZ, S. "WADEX: A New Tool in Literature Retrieving," *Mechanical Engineering,* Vol. 86, No. 3 (March, 1964), pp. 45–50.

SCHWEYER, H. E. "Graphs Can Reveal Project Feasibility," *Chemical Engineering,* Vol. 68 (September 18, 1961), pp. 175–78.

SULLIVAN, C. I. "CPI Management Looks at R and D Project Evaluation," *Industrial and Engineering Chemistry,* Vol. 53, No. 9 (September, 1961), pp. 42A–46A.

TYLER, C., AND WINTER, C. H., JR. *Chemical Engineering Economics,* 4th ed. New York: McGraw-Hill Book Co., Inc., 1959.

U.S. DEPARTMENT OF COMMERCE. *Developing and Selling New Products.* Washington, D.C.: Small Business Administration, 1955.

——— *Inventions Wanted by Armed Forces and Other Government Agencies.* Washington, D.C.: National Inventors Council, 1961.

WEAVER, J. B. "Appraisal of Development Projects," *Industrial and Engineering Chemistry,* Vol. 53, No. 12 (December, 1961), pp. 61A–62A.

Chapter 5—References

DALLY, JAMES W. "Serendipity or Design?" *Industrial Research* (November, 1963), pp. 38–43.

DuBRIDGE, L. A., "Explorers and Creators," *Mechanical Engineering* (October, 1953), pp. 796–98.

HYMAN, RAY. "Creativity," *International Science and Technology* (August, 1963), pp. 51–58.

KING, BLAKE. "Object: 'Creativity'," *Mechanical Engineering,* Vol. 85, No. 11 (November, 1963), pp. 38–41.

MANSFIELD, EDWIN. "Research and Technological Change," *Industrial Research* (February, 1964), pp. 25–28.

MATTHIAS, BERND. "Gambler in the Laboratory," *International Science and Technology* (June, 1964), pp. 32–37.

OLDS, B. S. "On the Mathematics of Committees, Boards and Panels," *Scientific Monthly,* Vol. 63 (1946), pp. 129–34.

REEL, H. C. "Thinking Unlimited," *Mechanical Engineering,* Vol. 86, No. 2 (February, 1964), pp. 30–31.

Research Conference on the Identification of Creative Scientific Talent—1959. (Also 1955 and 1957.) Salt Lake City: University of Utah Press, 1959.

Research is People. New York: Industrial Research Institute, Inc., and New York University Press, 1956.

SCHEERER, MARTIN. "Problem-Solving," *Scientific American,* Vol. 208, No. 4 (April, 1963), pp. 118–28.

SCHON, DONALD A. "Innovation by Invasion," *International Science and Technology* (March, 1964), pp. 52–60.

STARR, C. "Managing for Creativity," *Research/Development,* Vol. 12, No. 10 (October, 1961), pp. 25–34.

WILLIAMS, F. C. "How to Invent," *International Science and Technology* (February, 1964), pp. 49–53.

Chapter 6—References

Doing Business with the Federal Government. (A guide for the businessman.) General Services Administration, Washington, D. C. January, 1961.

"Expenditures," *Industrial Research* (January, 1964), pp. 36–39.

FEI, EDWARD C. "Research for International Aid," *Intertional Science and Technology* (December, 1962), pp. 52–57.

HANSEN, J. V. E. "The R & D Proposal," *Astronautics*, Vol. 5 (April, 1960), p. 39.

HOROWITZ, IRA, AND ALCOTT, J. A. *Small Business and Government Research and Development* (Small Business Management Series No. 28), Washington, D.C.: Small Business Administration.

STEEL, T. K. "How to Get Government R and D Contracts," *Industrial Research* (December, 1961), pp. 14–19.

U.S. DEPARTMENT OF COMMERCE. *Synopsis of U.S. Government Proposed Procurement, Sales, and Contract Awards.* Chicago, Ill.: Field Service, 433 West Van Buren Street.

U.S. DEPARTMENT OF DEFENSE. *Armed Service Procurement Regulations.* Latest Edition. Washington, D.C.

———— *Basic Research in the Air Force.* Washington, D.C.: Air Research and Development Command, Andrews Air Force Base, 1959.

———— *Contractors Guide Research and Development in the U.S. Army.* Washington, D.C.: Office of Chief, Research and Development, Department of the Army, 1959.

———— *Contract Research Program (ONR-1).* Washington, D.C.: Office of Naval Research, Department of the Navy, 1959.

———— *Industrial Security Manual for Safeguarding Classified Information.* Washington, D.C.: U.S. Government Printing Office.

———— *Technical Objective Document Release Program (RDR-121).* Washington, D.C.: Air Research and Development Command, Andrews Air Force Base, 1960 or later.

———— *U.S. Army Research and Development Problems Guide.*

Individual volumes may be secured by indicating your capabilities and security classifications to the following locations:

Volume

    I—U.S. Army Chemical Corps (SECRET)
    Commanding General
    U.S. Army Chemical Corps Research & Development
      Command
    Building T-7, Gravelly Point
    Washington 25, D.C.

    II—U.S. Army Engineer Corps (CONFIDENTIAL)
    Commanding General
    U.S. Army Engineer Research & Development Laboratories
    Fort Belvoir, Virginia

    III—U.S. Army Medical Corps (UNCLASSIFIED)
    Commanding General
    U.S. Army Medical Research & Development Command
    Main Navy Building
    Washington 25, D.C.

    IV—U.S. Army Ordnance Corps (SECRET)
    Address Commanding Officer, nearest Ordnance District Office

    V—U.S. Army Quartermaster Corps (UNCLASSIFIED)
    Commanding General
    U.S. Army Quartermaster Research & Engineering Command
    Natick, Massachusetts

    VI—U.S. Army Signal Corps (CONFIDENTIAL)
    Commanding General
    U.S. Army Signal Research & Development Laboratory
    Fort Monmouth, New Jersey

    VII—U.S. Army Transportation Corps (UNCLASSIFIED)
    Commanding General
    U.S. Army Transportation Research Command
    Fort Eustis, Virginia

    VIII—Army Research Office (UNCLASSIFIED)
    Commanding General
    Army Research Office

4000 Arlington Blvd.
Arlington Hall Station
Arlington, Virginia

WOODROW, RAYMOND J. "Grants Vs. Contracts," *Industrial Research* (April, 1964), pp. 48–57.

Chapter 7—References

ARCHIBALD, R. D., AND VILLORIA, R. L. "Project Planning and Evaluation," *Mechanical Engineering,* Vol. 86, No. 6 (June, 1964), pp. 48–51.

BROWNLEE, K. A., *Industrial Experimentation.* 2nd ed. Brooklyn: Chemical Publishing Co., 1948.

COCHRAN, W. G., AND COX, G. M. *Experimental Designs.* 1st and 2nd eds. New York: John Wiley and Sons, 1950 and 1957.

COMSTOCK, DANIEL F. "How to Buy Contract Research," *Industrial Research* (November, 1963), pp. 26–27.

DAVIES, O. L. (ed.). *Design and Analysis of Industrial Experiments.* New York: Hafner Publishing Co., 1956.

FALCONER, DAVID, AND NEVILL, GALE. "Critical Path Diagramming," *International Science and Technology* (October, 1962), pp. 43–49.

FUCHS, I. J. "Product Failure: Causes and Preventions," *Mechanical Engineering,* Vol. 86, No. 2 (February, 1964), pp. 36–39.

FULLER, F. H. "The Human Machine—Work & Environment," *Mechanical Engineering,* Vol. 85, No. 12 (December, 1963), pp. 22–26.

HALCOMB, J. L. "PERT in Product Design," *Mechanical Engineering,* Vol. 85, No. 5 (May, 1963), pp. 34–37.

HAWKINS, G. A., AND BOELTER, L. M. K. "Engineering Mode of Analysis," *Mechanical Engineering* (October, 1953), pp. 799–808.

HOLMSTROM, J. E. *Records and Research in Engineering and Industrial Science.* London: Chapman and Hall, 1956.

KEMPTHORNE, O. *The Design and Analysis of Experiments.* New York: John Wiley and Sons, 1952.

LAZIER, W. A. "Planning the Research Project," *Proceedings of the Sixth Annual Conference on the Administration of Research,* pp. 59–63. Atlanta: Georgia Institute of Technology, 1953.

LIVINGSTON, J. S. "PERT in Research Management," *Industrial Research* (June, 1963) , pp. 22–25.

LYNN, H., JR. "How to Be a Project Leader—Nine Helpful Hints," *Operations Research,* Vol. 4 (1956) , pp. 484–88.

MANN, H. B. *Analysis and Design of Experiments.* New York: Dover Publications, 1949.

MASSON, H. J. "Training and Planning in Research," *Proceedings of the Sixth Annual Conference on the Administration of Research,* pp. 69–72. Atlanta: Georgia Institute of Technology, 1953.

MCCRORY, R. J. "The Design Method," *Mechanical Engineering,* Vol. 85, No. 5 (May, 1963) , pp. 30–31.

PAPPAS, G. F., AND MACLAREN, D. D. "An Approach to Research Planning," *Chemical Engineering Progress,* Vol. 57, No. 5 (May, 1961) , pp. 65–69.

PELZ, DONALD C. "Freedom in Research," *International Science and Technology* (February, 1964) , pp. 54–66.

PERRY, JOHN. *Human Relations in Small Industry.* Washington, D.C.: Small Defense Plants Administration, March, 1953.

RUBENSTEIN, A. H. (ed.) . "Coordination, Control and Financing of Industrial Research," *Proceedings of the Fifth Annual Conference on Industrial Research, June, 1954.* New York: King's Crown Press, 1955.

SANDOR, G. N. "The Seven Stages of Engineering Design," *Mechanical Engineering,* Vol. 86, No. 4 (April, 1964) , pp. 21–25.

THORNDIKE, R. L. *Research Problems and Techniques.* Washington, D.C.: U.S. Government Printing Office, 1947.

TOWNES, C. H. "Doing Research," *International Science and Technology* (March, 1964) , pp. 35–39.

VAN VECHTEN, C. C. "Value Engineering—Functional Attack on Costs," *Mechanical Engineering,* Vol. 85, No. 11 (November, 1963), pp. 35–37.

Chapter 8—References

An ASME Paper. A.S.M.E. Manual MS-4. New York: The American Society of Mechanical Engineers, February 1956.

BROWNLEE, K. A. *Industrial Experimentation,* 2nd ed. Brooklyn: Chemical Publishing Co., 1948.

DAVIES, O. L. (ed.). *Design and Analysis of Industrial Experiments.* New York: Hafner Publishing Co., 1956.

HOLMSTROM, J. E. *Records and Research in Engineering and Industrial Science.* London: Chapman and Hall, 1956.

HUNTER, LAURA GRACE. *The Language of Audit Reports.* Washington, D.C.: United States General Accounting Office, 1957.

KEMPTHORNE, O. *The Design and Analysis of Experiments.* New York: John Wiley and Sons, 1952.

MANN, H. B. *Analysis and Design of Experiments.* New York: Dover Publications, 1949.

Presentation of Ideas. Washington, D.C.: Administrative Office, Publications Division, Department of the Navy, 1955.

ROGERS, CARL R., AND ROETHLISBERGER, F. J. "Barriers and Gateways to Communication," *Harvard Business Review* (July–August, 1952), pp. 28–34.

U.S. DEPARTMENT OF HEALTH, EDUCATION, AND WELFARE. *Getting Your Ideas Across Through Writing.* Training Manual No. 7. Washington, D.C., 1950.

WEINBERG, ALVIN M. "Scientific Communication," *International Science and Technology* (April, 1963), pp. 65–74.

Chapter 9—References

CADE, W. M., AND COLEMAN, R. N. "Product Testing: Simulating the Field Conditions," *Mechanical Engineering,* Vol. 86, No. 2 (February, 1964), pp. 32–35.

DAVIS, ALBERT S., JR. "A Piece of the Action," *International Science and Technology* (December, 1963), pp. 49–53.

GILFOIL, W. S., AND RASMUSSEN, L. E. "Engineering Assistance to Research and Development," *Industrial and Engineering Chemistry,* Vol. 50, No. 9 (1958), pp. 62A–64A.

GRANZEIER, FRANK J. "The Competitive Advantage," *Industrial Research* (November, 1963), pp. 63–67.

MORTON, JACK A. "From Research to Technology," *International Science and Technology* (May, 1964), pp. 82–92.

U.S. DEPARTMENT OF COMMERCE. *Developing and Selling New Products.* Washington, D.C.: Small Business Administration, 1955.

———— *Patents and Inventions—An Information Aid for Inventors.* Washington, D.C.: Patent Office, 1959.

Chapter 1—Problems

1. Define production, applied research, developmental research, and basic research.

2. What is the genesis of a new product for commercialization?

3. What is the chain reaction associated with basic research?

4. To be successful should a company perform fundamental, applied, and developmental research? Explain.

5. Should basic research projects be outlined in detail prior to funding? Explain your reasoning and give justifications for your answer.

6. Is it realistic to expect research expenditures to increase indefinitely? Give the basis for your answer.

7. Which industries account for over 80 percent of the federal research and development funds expended by industry?

8. Give the ratio of basic research to total R and D for the aerospace, chemical process, and machinery industries.

9. In 1961, the aerospace industry spent approximately 24 percent of its net sales on research and development. Was this expenditure funded from profits of the company? If not, where did the funds come from?

10. What is the average expenditure from company funds for research and development in progressive industries?

Chapter 2—Problems

1. Before embarking upon a research and development program what are the most important factors to consider?

2. Of the factors given in 1, which one do you consider most important? Why?

3. Why does developmental research require administrative control?

4. Is it possible for scientists to be more creative if they are influenced by several echelons of decision-making influences? Explain your reasoning in detail.

5. What is the product of an academically organized research operation? Explain.

6. What is the product of the private research organization? Explain.

7. What advantage does a private research organization have over an educational research organization? Is this really an advantage?

8. How can a corporation maximize its research expenditures?

9. What is the difference between a horizontal and vertical type of organization? Explain fully and indicate the advantages and disadvantages of each.

10. What are the main ingredients necessary to assure the survival of a research organization? Explain how each ingredient affects the overall organization.

Chapter 3—Problems

1. What is the most important characteristic of a good research administrator?

2. What percentage of engineers are utilized in research and development?

3. What is an important characteristic for an engineer if he wishes to pursue a career in research and development? Explain your answer.

4. What is the most important task for a research manager? How will this task bear upon the success of his research effort?

5. What characteristics are found in the creative individual? Describe each and indicate how it might contribute to creativity.

6. Organize a recruiting program for research and de-

velopment engineers. Describe in detail the process you would use to assure that your company had a continuing supply of creative, young, and enthusiastic engineers and scientists.

7. List some of the intangible costs of maintaining a researcher.

8. In what areas do management and research differ? Who makes final decisions?

9. Describe the differences between the self-employed professional and the employee professional. In what way are they similar? Describe in detail.

10. How is the cost of maintaining a research and development scientist related to company size? What industry has the lowest cost? Why? What industry has the highest cost? Why?

Chapter 4—Problems

1. What factors make government-funded research and development programs dangerous to the well being of an industrial company? Explain how the factors affect the company's operation.

2. In determining the orientation of a research program what items should receive careful consideration? Itemize all the items you can think of and indicate why they are important.

3. The feasibility of establishing a research division in an organization concerns what important considerations? Why are these items important?

4. A company has unobligated funds of $25,000. Should they embark upon a new internal research effort which will require the talents of several disciplines? List the assumptions backing up your answer. Also list an alternate solution.

5. A company making aircraft and missiles has a net sales volume of two hundred million dollars. What amount of company funds can this company reasonably expect to put into research and development? If

the funds can be supplemented by government contracts how much could an average company expect to
obtain from this source? Would this type of research
effort be desirable from the company's standpoint?
Why?

6. A qualitative rating for an R and D project indicates
the following:

   a. Payoff period of project is 50 percent of the permissible payoff period.

   b. The estimated cash position of the project after
   ten years is 50 percent of the most optimistic
   value.

   c. The chances of success for the project are fair.

   d. The project can have an advantageous competitive position in regard to raw materials, sales,
   manpower, early market penetration, and
   product life.

   Would you consider the above R and D project
   promising? Why?

7. Determine a final rating for the above project, using
Sullivan's project evaluation system (See *Ind. Eng.
Chem.*, 53, 42A [1961]) and adding other assump-
tions as necessary.

8. A subsystem on a complicated research and development project is completed six months before schedule. Is this the result of good planning? Explain
your answer in detail.

9. A large research project is contemplated by top
management. Unfortunately, this project requires
that a new material be developed in order for the
project to be successful. The possibility of developing the material is open to debate. The material
researchers of the company are confident that they
can come up with the desired product; however,
other scientists are skeptical. How should top management go about handling the funding of such a
project if it is decided to proceed? Explain in detail
how you would propose to handle this situation.

10. Do you feel that market surveys are necessary before

industrial research and development programs are started? Explain.

11. Under what conditions is it possible to eliminate market surveys without detriment to the company's well-being? Explain.

Chapter 5—Problems

1. Are all persons basically creative? What method is available to determine whether or not a person is creative? From your own experience concoct a method for determining creativity and indicate how you would use it.

2. Define creativity. Is a person creative if he has a lot of ideas but never does anything with them? Explain your reasoning.

3. What distinguishes the creative individual from the noncreative? Can creativity be enhanced by education and training? Is it possible that too much formal education, for instance, a Ph.D. program of study, may be a detriment to the creative process? Explain your reasoning.

4. What are the characteristics of the creative mental process? Are these characteristics sufficient to assure creative ideas? Explain.

5. What part do imagination and enlightenment play in the creative process? Define each term and indicate an example of each.

6. Is it possible for environment to stifle the highly creative individual? What variation of creativity do you think is possible? Explain your reasoning.

7. Can completely noncreative individuals be trained to be creative? Can an environment of creativity stimulate latent creative talents? Explain.

8. Of the three most important tasks of a research administrator in the management of creative endeavor, which do you think is most important and why?

9. What factors are important in establishing an environment for creativity? Explain.

10. What is *brain storming* and how is it used? Give an example of a problem and indicate how you would go about solving it, if you have been unsuccessful in obtaining answers from individuals in your organization. Why would your method succeed? Explain in detail.

Chapter 6—Problems

1. What is a proposal and why is it necessary? Explain.

2. Should a proposal contain a bibliography or should it contain all the basic information in detail? Explain.

3. Itemize the five features of a skillfully prepared proposal and define each in your own words. Do you feel that the features are redundant? Explain.

4. Is it important for a scientist or researcher to be able to speak and write correctly? Why?

5. Name five government agencies which sponsor research and identify topics of interest for each. What makes up the Department of Defense?

6. How would you go about finding out where to submit a research proposal on the "sex life of a nematode"?

7. Prepare two biographical sketches of yourself for incorporation in research proposals. In one be strictly factual and give data precisely. In the other, still being factual, amplify your best characteristics and create a biographical sketch which makes you an interesting individual.

8. Write a proposal to conduct an exhaustive literature search on the various types of automobile transmissions which are available. Estimate the cost of the work and detail how you would go about doing it. Include your biographical sketch. Also determine to

whom the proposal should be sent and write a cover letter enclosing the proposal to this agency. Consider that you work for a research organization of a university.

9. What is a *hard-sell?* Should research proposals be sold like refrigerators? Explain your reasoning.

10. What is an *unsolicited industrial proposal?* What precautions should be taken when selling research to small industrial organizations? Explain.

Chapter 7—Problems

1. What are desirable characteristics for a project director?

2. What is the prime responsibility of the project director?

3. What is a milestone?

4. Are progress reports of value or are they just tedious chores to keep the project director busy? Explain the purpose of the progress report and what it should contain.

5. What is an S-curve and what does it tell the project director?

6. List the characteristics of a good project director. Explain why you think these characteristics are desirable or undesirable?

7. What is involved in the investigative procedure? What is an analytical solution? What is an experimental or empirical solution?

8. Why is it necessary for some experimental information to be available before attempting an analytical solution to a complex problem?

9. What is a research tool? Are research tools necessary for all types of research? Explain.

10. Why is research necessary to civilization?

11. Should the purchase of research tools be predicated

on an immediate economic gain? Should the purchase of research tools have any economic implica-
tion? Explain.

Chapter 8—Problems

1. What is a progress report? Is it important to submit
   progress reports on time? When would it be permissible to submit a progress report after its due date?

2. What is the most important ingredient in getting a
   report out on time? Are the results described in the
   report important to the contracting officer of the
   sponsor? Why?

3. What is the difference between a technical report
   and the journal article? Why should research results
   be published in journals?

4. Is it important that the researcher publish his results
   in journals if the technical report is listed in DDC
   or other summaries? Explain.

5. Why is it important that the technical report contain
   in detail descriptions of all the facets of the research?

6. Is it possible for valuable research to be lost to
   posterity? How could this occur with the current
   information explosion? Explain.

7. How does a researcher use a literature research
   group? In your opinion what is the value of this
   service?

8. Why is it necessary to get permission from the
   sponsor before publishing in a recognized journal?
   How should this permission be given?

9. Does submission of a journal article insure publication? Why do large research organizations monitor
   the articles being submitted for publication by their
   staffs?

10. How would you start writing a paper for publica-
    tion? Explain.

11. Why do industrial sponsors of research often prevent

publications of their research results? Do you feel they are justified?

Chapter 9—Problems

1. Why must research results be put to work?
2. How can research results be protected? Describe briefly the methods.
3. What are *trade secrets?* Is it possible to keep *trade secrets* secret?
4. Should every patentable item or result be patented? Explain.
5. Is it important to keep good records on research leading to possible inventions? Why?
6. What is a patent search? Where is it conducted?
7. What is a patent claim?
8. How can a new product be marketed if the parent company has no production facilities or sales outlets?
9. When may it be feasible for the parent company to embark on a production facility building program? How would a company with limited personnel go about obtaining the new facility?
10. What factors are important in deciding the method of production and distribution of a new product?
11. What are royalties? What is a licensee? What is a licensor?
12. What is meant by market development?
13. How do research results generate more research work?
14. Is research important for industrial survival? Why?

Index

229

*This book has been set in 12 point
Baskerville, leaded 3 points, and 11
point Baskerville, leaded 2 points.
Chapter numbers are 14 point Baskerville italic, and chapter titles are
24 point Baskerville roman. The
size of the type page is 24 x 44½
picas.*